T3-AMD-988

a/18/14
18/18/14

J
292

The Golden treasury
of myths and legends.

APR 15 1995   651

201513   Lakeside Joint School Dist,
              19621 Black Road
              Los Gatos, Ca. 95030

SANTA CLARA VALLEY LIBRARY SYSTEM
Mountain View Public Library
Santa Clara County Free Library
California

Alum Rock   Milpitas   (Calaveras
                                        (Community Center
                                        (Sunnyhills
Campbell   Morgan Hill
Cupertino   Saratoga   (Quito
Gilroy   (Village
Los Altos   Stanford-Escondido

Central Research Library Headquarters
For Bookmobile Service, request schedule

MYTHS AND LEGENDS

H595595

du saint
giziae.
mouſt n
mezueu
que ann
in neb
zent que

hpod ꝼapi maꝛel
helm ſcyldinga ic
Inne eide emhe
peſende paɼ hu
caldɼo ſep. eczpɼo
haꝛen ꝺcin ꞇo noſt

A+M.P.
1958

aicel nr ure
crccrf eft l
uamime
efpanetr

THE GOLDEN TREASURY OF

MYTHS

AND
LEGENDS

ADAPTED FROM THE WORLD'S GREAT
CLASSICS BY ANNE TERRY WHITE

ILLUSTRATED BY
ALICE AND MARTIN PROVENSEN

GOLDEN PRESS   NEW YORK

201513

Santa Clara County Free Library
San Jose. California
Schools Division

NINTH PRINTING, 1969

© COPYRIGHT 1959 BY WESTERN PUBLISHING COMPANY, INC. ALL RIGHTS RE-
SERVED, INCLUDING THE RIGHT OF REPRODUCTION IN WHOLE OR IN PART IN ANY
FORM. PRINTED IN THE U.S.A. PUBLISHED BY GOLDEN PRESS, NEW YORK, N.Y.

CONTENTS

GODS AND HEROES

THE ANCIENT Greeks were an amazingly creative people. They looked at the stars and saw pictures—a bear, a lion, a swan, a giant, a bull, a scorpion. They looked at the sun and imagined it to be a fiery chariot driven daily across the sky. They saw the jagged lightning and said: "Zeus the Thunderer is hurling his thunderbolts."

Whatever had motion seemed to them to be alive. There were deathless beings inhabiting the sky and the sea, the rivers and the springs and the quivering groves. In cave and grotto, on mountain top and in the deep interior of the mysterious earth, immortal beings dwelt. Anyone could see them. And nearly everyone did. They saw sea-nymphs rising on the foamy waves, dryads gliding among the trees, naiads sporting in the lakes and streams. The delightful creatures were very near, very familiar.

And so were the greater gods. For the Greeks had made them all in their own image. Except that they were more powerful and did not die, the Greek gods and goddesses were scarcely different from themselves. Mortals and *im*mortals, that was how the Greeks distinguished between human beings and the gods—men died, the gods lived forever.

The Greeks had many gods. And when after long centuries the Romans met and finally conquered the Greeks, they took their gods over and worshiped them under Roman names. They called the king of the gods Jupiter instead of Zeus. They called the queen of heaven Juno instead of Hera. Poseidon, who ruled the sea, became Neptune. Ares, god of war, became Mars. Aphrodite, goddess of beauty and love, was changed to Venus. Wherever the Romans went as conquerors, they dotted the earth with temples to these gods.

Today the gods of the Greeks and Romans do not have a single temple. They do not have a single worshiper. But they are immortal. They cannot die because the Greeks

invented such wonderful myths about them.

Some of these myths seek to explain the mystery of growth and death, the why of the seasons, day and night, the meaning of echo. Some are myths of origin. Where did man come from? Who taught him to use fire? How did evil get into the world? Others, again, relate the adventures of heroes like Hercules and Perseus and Theseus, who were ideals to copy, but very human ones. They fought for what they held to be the right—loved, hated, sinned, and won glory everlasting.

Certain of the stories you will read here are legends, not myths. And the difference lies in this: a myth is an invented story, while a legend is not wholly an invented story—it is a kind of history. Of course, there may be plenty of invention and myth wrapped around a legend, but always at its heart there is a kernel of historical truth.

Now sometimes what was thought to be a myth is suddenly understood to be a legend, as in the case of Theseus who slew the bull monster Minotaur in the Labyrinth and saved the Greek captives from a terrible death.

In the early 1900's Arthur Evans found the ruins of a palace in Crete. It looked very much like a maze, or labyrinth. But when it was restored, the magnificence of its staircases and corridors and bathrooms astonished the world. In many places on the walls were the marks of the *labrys,* or two-headed ax, which was the symbol of Cretan Zeus. Evans found a wall painting showing a youth doing a back somersault over a bull while a girl held out her hands to catch him. This was the source of the tribute story. The Athenian youths and maidens were not fed to the Bull of Minos. They were trained to be performers in the dangerous bull-vaulting ceremonies honoring Cretan Zeus.

Many lands have contributed legends to this book. *Sigurd of the Volsungs* is about those bold seafarers, the Vikings, who in the year 1000 discovered America. The tale of Sigurd and his father Sigmund was written down in Iceland a century or two after that great journey. But the minstrels had sung it in the courts of many kings for hundreds of years before, for the Volsungs were part of a very old store of European legends. So

9

was *Beowulf*. Although this is the first poem in the English language, its hero is a Dane and his fights with monsters and a fiery dragon took place in Denmark and Sweden.

Tristram and Iseult is a Celtic legend. It was recorded in French, and then in English, and at first was not part of the King Arthur story at all. Now, legends as a rule stop growing when people no longer believe in them. But this story is so gripping that it has never stopped. Wagner composed an opera about the lovers and a modern American poet, Edwin Arlington Robinson, wrote a long poem about them.

Rustem and Sohrab is Persian. It was told for centuries before the Persian poet Firdausi wrote it down around the year 1000. So Rustem and Sohrab were heroes of the same time as the Volsungs, but living in a much more civilized land. And this the legends clearly show. The Viking tale is harsh as granite, the Persian is like marble.

The Battle of Roncevaux is French. There really was a Roland. And a rear guard under him really was wiped out in a mountain pass. But that took place long before the time of Charlemagne. When the French began to tell the glories of their great king who fought the Saracens in Spain, they made Roland part of Charlemagne's story. The treason of Ganelon is all invented. It was put in to show that Roland and his comrades were so brave that they could be defeated only by treason.

Every legend in this book is different, yet in one way all are alike. Each is built around an unusual personality who is larger than the rest—braver, stronger of build, mightier in handling spear or sword. For to the people who first told these tales, physical prowess was more admirable than anything else. Today other ways of achieving fame are open to us. But we still admire physical prowess. That is why when we read about the courage and skill of these heroes, we have the same sense of excitement as did the people who first heard the legends. We have the same sense of lift when they conquer. We feel the same sadness when they come to grief. For man remains unchanged in one respect: no matter how the world he lives in changes, we are all hero-worshipers at heart—today no less than in the days of old.

10

PROMETHEUS STEALS FIRE FROM HEAVEN

THERE was a time when there were no gods. Heaven and Earth alone existed. They were the first parents, and from their union sprang the gigantic Titans. For ages the Titans ruled the world. But at last the gods, who were the children of the Titans, rebelled and overthrew them. Then it was that Zeus became supreme ruler of the universe and his wife and sister, Hera, became queen of heaven.

Now as yet there were no men on earth, and none of the animals seemed worthy to rule the rest. So the gods decided to make still another kind of creature. One of the Titans, Prometheus—whose name means Forethought—was chosen for the task.

Down from heaven the Titan sped. He took clay and mixed it with water, kneaded it, and shaped it in the likeness of the gods. He made his creature stand upright, for he wanted man to look up at the stars and not down on the earth, like the animals. Then Prometheus thought:

"What gifts shall I give this work of my hands to make him superior to the rest of creation?"

Unfortunately, his brother Epimetheus—which means Afterthought—had already given all the great gifts to the animals. Strength and courage, cunning and speed—he had distributed them all. Wings, claws, horns, scales, shelly covering—nothing was left for man.

Then quick-witted Prometheus thought of fire. Oh, great and wonderful gift! "With fire," the Titan thought, "man can make weapons and subdue the beasts, forge tools, plow the earth, and master the arts. What matter that my creature has neither fur nor feathers, scales nor shell? Fire will warm his dwelling, and he need fear neither rain nor snow nor the wild north wind."

Back to heaven Prometheus sped, lit his torch at the chariot of the sun, brought down fire to man, and went away rejoicing.

But up on high Olympus, great Zeus frowned as he sat with the gods feasting on nectar and ambrosia. For Zeus was ever jealous of his power.

"This creature that looks to heaven is truly more than a match for the beasts," he thought. "Indeed, he is almost a match for the gods. But I will curb his ill-got power!"

Straightway Zeus made woman, lovely as a goddess. All the immortals bestowed gifts upon her to make her yet more captivating. And they called her Pandora—Gift-of-all. When she was finished, Zeus himself bore the dazzling creature to the Titans.

"Beware!" Prometheus cautioned his brothers. "I fear the gifts of wily Zeus. He bears me ill will because of the fire I stole from heaven and brought down to mankind."

But Epimetheus was enchanted with Pandora and took her to his heart and home.

Now in that home Epimetheus had a jar in which he kept certain gifts he had not distributed among the animals when he had made them. He took great pains to tell Pandora she must leave this jar alone. "On no account must you open it," he warned her.

But, above all things else, the gods had endowed Pandora with curiosity. No sooner was she alone than she sped to the forbidden jar.

"Surely it will do no harm if I just peek in and see what is there," thought she.

She slipped off the cover. And there flew out a host of evil plagues and all manner of disease, envy, spite, revenge—and scattered themselves far and wide. Pandora clapped on the lid. But it was too late. The jar was all but empty. Only hope had remained— hope which never leaves mankind.

There was no danger now that man would rival the gods—he had enemies far worse than wild beasts to contend with. But still Zeus could not forgive Prometheus.

"The thief who stole heaven's fire shall be punished as his love of man deserves!" Zeus declared. "He shall be chained to the highest rock of Mount Caucasus—where man can never climb. Scorched by the sun, he shall lie and groan. And I shall cause a vulture to prey upon his liver, which shall grow again as fast as it is devoured."

He summoned Hephaestus. And high on the mountain where eagles make their home, heaven's lame smith—all unwilling—riveted the Titan to the rock. There Prometheus hung in his chains. But he neither groaned nor besought pity, neither regretted what he had done nor bent his knee before the tyrant. The rock, the vulture, and the chain—all that the proud can feel of pain—he endured, and showed his agony to none.

A MIRACLE ON MOUNT PARNASSUS

Man's first years on earth were very happy ones—they were a Golden Age in which truth and right prevailed. Then came the Silver Age, and after it, the Age of Brass, each worse than the one before. But worse still was the Iron Age that followed. So wicked had man grown by this time that the whole earth was drenched with blood. Brothers and sisters, husbands and wives, no longer trusted one another. Sons wished their fathers dead that they might inherit their wealth. The guest was not safe in the house of his friend. And the gods were entirely neglected.

At last Zeus could endure it no longer and calling the gods in council, he thus addressed them:

"Immortals! No longer does the sweet smell of roasted flesh rise from the sacrifices to the nostrils of the gods. Mankind does not honor the deathless ones. The altars are strewn with cold ashes, the temples are empty. I will destroy this infamous race of men! I will people the earth anew, with a race more worthy of life, with beings who will know what is due the gods!"

The Thunderer spoke his will and rose. He was about to unleash his lightnings and scorch the earth when he remembered that from so great a blaze the sky itself might catch fire. "I will drown mankind instead," he decided.

Chaining up the winds that scatter clouds, he sent the South Wind alone to cloak the sky with inky blackness. The thunder rolled. Rain streamed in torrents from the heavens. Poseidon meantime caused the earth to quake and mountainous waves to overwhelm the shore. Then he called upon the rivers:

"Loose your currents! Sweep away houses! Uproot orchards! Burst the dams!"

The rivers obeyed. Swollen with rain, they overflowed.

And now the fields were drowned and the harvests ruined. Trees were torn up by the roots. Flocks, herds, houses, barns, everything was swept into the swirling flood. The land had turned into a raging sea. Wild beasts, grown tame, shared the heights with man. And still the floods rose and overwhelmed them all.

Mount Parnassus alone topped the waves. And there an old man and his aged wife had taken refuge. He was Prometheus' son, Deucalion, an upright man. His wife was Pandora's daughter, Pyrrha, a pious woman who had always honored the gods. Warned by Prometheus of the coming flood, the couple had reached the mountain in a sturdy boat.

The sight of the two old people, last of all mankind, touched the heart of angry Zeus. His rage was stilled at last. "These two have lived blameless lives," he thought. "And

13

they shall not be destroyed. It is enough!"

He unchained the winds in order that they might sweep away the clouds while Poseidon, his brother, smoothed the waves with his trident. The overflowing rivers returned to their channels. And heaven and earth beheld each other again.

Peace. Stillness. Light after darkness. The terrible price of wickedness paid . . .

"Oh wife!" Deucalion cried, clasping his helpless hands as he looked about at the slime-covered earth, all littered with the bodies of the dead. "Would that my father had taught me his art! Would that we, too, could make men out of clay. But since we cannot, let us turn to the gods and ask them what remains for us to do."

A ruined altar of the goddess of justice stood a little distance away. Hand in hand they made their way to it and fell on their knees before the fireless hearth. "Tell us, O goddess," they cried, "what we must do!"

Immediately a voice answered them. "Go from my altar! Veil your heads, loose your garments from your limbs, and cast behind you the bones of your mother."

Deucalion and Pyrrha heard the awful words in astonishment. For a time they were too terrified to speak. Then Pyrrha said:

"Forgive us, great goddess, if we shudder and do not obey you. We dare not profane the bones of our parents."

They left the altar and entered the shade of the woods to think over the words of the oracle. All at once a light struck Deucalion.

"Wife!" he cried, "The command is one we may obey! For is not the earth the mother of all? The stones are her bones. We may cast them behind us! This is what the oracle means, I think. Anyway, it will do no harm to try."

So they veiled their faces and unbound their garments. They picked up stones and threw them over their shoulders. And wonder of wonders! The stones grew and took rude shape, like blocks of marble as yet unfinished by the hands of the sculptor.

The stones that Pyrrha threw became women. Those thrown by Deucalion became men. And a hardy race took over the earth, a race well fitted for toil and labor—even as we are today.

PHAETHON AND THE HORSES OF THE SUN

YOUNG Phaethon was in a rage. His
schoolmates had been making fun of
him, laughing at the idea that he was
the son of a god. But he was, he was! His
mother, the sea nymph Clymene, had many
times told him so.

"There is your glorious father," she had
said, pointing to the glistening Sun. "See how
skillfully he drives his fiery chariot!"

Flushed with shame and anger, Phaethon
stood now before Clymene. "If I am indeed
of heavenly birth, mother, give me some
proof of it!" he pleaded.

"What proof can I give you?" Clymene
answered. Then she stretched her hands upward to the skies. "I call to witness the Sun
which looks down upon us, that I have told
you the truth," she said solemnly. "If I speak
falsely, let this be the last time I behold his
light! But," she added, "why don't you go
and ask him yourself? The land where the
Sun rises lies next to ours. Go and ask Apollo
whether he will own you for his son."

Phaethon's face lit up. Without delay he set

off for India, and not long afterwards stood
before the glittering palace of the Sun.

His heart beat with pride and hope and
wonder as he gazed upon the lofty columns,
all ablaze with precious stones, at the ceilings
of polished ivory, the doors of silver. Yet he
hardly paused to look at the splendid scenes
of earth and sky and sea which Hephaestus
had cunningly wrought upon the walls.
Phaethon was too impatient to behold the
god. He ran lightly up the steps and went on
into the great hall. There, however, he was
forced to halt—the light was so dazzling he
could not bear it. At the other end of the hall
he could make out the god, clad in purple
raiment, seated on a throne glittering with
diamonds. And on either side stood his attendants. They were the Day, the Month,
the Year, the Hours, and the Seasons—
Spring crowned with flowers, Summer
decked with sheaves of yellow grain, Au-
tumn stained with wine, and Winter with
snowy locks.

The great god saw the youth standing by

the door and called out to him, "What brings you here?"

"O light of the boundless world, Phoebus my father—if you will let me use that honored name—" the youth blurted out, "I am Phaethon. Give me, I implore you, some proof by which men may know that I am indeed your son."

Apollo laid aside the blinding rays of light about his head.

"Approach, my son," he said, and embraced Phaethon warmly. "I confirm what your mother has told you. But to put an end to your doubts, ask of me anything in the world that you want. I swear by the river Styx, upon which all gods take their oath,

that I will grant you whatever you desire."

"Then, father," Phaethon quickly replied, "let me drive the chariot of the Sun for just one day."

Phoebus Apollo shook his radiant head four times, so taken aback was he by the request.

"I have spoken rashly," he said, and his voice was deep with regret. "This one request I would deny. I beg you, Phaethon—choose something else. What you ask is not suited to your years and strength. None but myself— not even Zeus who hurls the thunderbolts— may drive the flaming car of day, and even for me it is not easy. The road is so steep at the start that the horses can scarcely climb it, fresh though they are at dawn. Midway, the course is so high above the earth that often as I stand upright in my chariot I get dizzy and dare not look down. And the last part of the way drops so sharply that the sea gods waiting to receive me at my journey's end wonder how it is I do not fall. If I lent you my chariot, what would you do? You think the road lies among the delightful dwellings of the gods. But no, it passes through the midst of frightful monsters—the Bull, the Lion, the Scorpion, and the Crab. Nor will you find it easy to control the horses. Do not insist, my son. You ask proof that you are my own. Are not my fears for you proof enough? The oath is sworn and I must keep it, but I beg you—choose more wisely! Look around the world. Choose what you will that is most precious, and it shall be yours. Only do not ask to drive the chariot."

Phaethon listened. But his mind was closed, and he would not change his request. So, much against his will, Apollo led him to where the chariot stood.

It, too, was the work of Hephaestus' hands, and dazzling to behold. Axle, pole, and wheels were all of gold, the spokes were of silver, the seat sparkled with rows of chrysolites and diamonds. But there was not time to examine the gleaming chariot, for

already Dawn had thrown open the doors
of the east. The stars faded, the earth began
to glow. The Moon gave the command to
harness the horses, and the Hours led the
four winged beasts out of their lofty stalls.

Phoebus took out a vial. With his own
hands he rubbed his son's face with the pro-
tective salve, then set the rays upon his head.

"Spare the whip," were the god's words to
Phaethon. "The horses go fast enough of
themselves. And hold the reins tight. Follow
the marks of the wheels. Do not go too high
or you will burn the dwellings of the gods,
nor too low lest you set the earth on fire. I
leave you now to your fate. Take the reins—
we can delay no longer."

Stammering his thanks, Phaethon sprang
into the chariot and grasped the reins. If only
his schoolmates could see him now!

In a moment, the boundless plain of the
universe lay before him. The spirited horses
dashed through the clouds, outrunning the
morning breeze. But soon they felt that
strange hands were guiding them. Snorting,
they rushed headlong and left the traveled
road. The chariot swung wildly from side to
side and up and down, while Phaethon looked
toward the earth and grew pale. His knees
shook, his head swam, his eyes were dim.

He wished that he had heeded his father
and never entered the chariot. But now he
had no choice. He had to go on, carried along
like a ship that flies before the tempest.

His eyes wide with terror, he looked
around him. He wanted to call out to the
horses, but he had forgotten their names. His
heart pounded like a hammer, while he tried
to think of what to do. Should he draw the
reins tight, or let them loose? Even as he
hesitated, they slipped from his trembling
hands. The wild steeds, feeling no restraint,
dashed off into the unknown regions of high
heaven, then plunged down almost to the
earth. The clouds smoked, the mountain tops

took fire, the fields were parched with heat.
Great cities and whole countries began to
burn. The entire world was on fire.

Phaethon saw the flames, and felt the un-
bearable heat. The air he breathed was like a
roaring furnace. The smoke was so thick
that down on earth the skins of the Ethiopians turned black. The sea shrank and the
fishes sought the lowest depths.

At last Earth could endure no more and
cried out to Zeus, "O ruler of the gods, save
what yet remains to us from the devouring
flame!"

Then mighty Zeus rose to his high tower
and filled the air with thunder. Brandishing
a lightning bolt, he hurled it at the charioteer
and struck him from his seat. Phaethon fell
headlong. His hair all on fire, he sped to
earth, flaring like a shooting star. . . . And far
below, Eridanus, the great river, received his
charred and broken body.

THE BRIDE OF PLUTO

Deep under Mt. Aetna, the gods had buried alive a number of fearful, fire-breathing giants. The monsters heaved and struggled to get free. And so mightily did they shake the earth that Pluto, the king of the underworld, was alarmed.

"They may tear the rocks asunder and leave the realm of the dead open to the light of day," he thought. And mounting his golden chariot, he went up to see what damage had been done.

Now the goddess of love and beauty, fair Aphrodite, was sitting on a mountainside playing with her son, Eros. She saw Pluto as he drove around with his coal-black horses and she said:

"My son, there is one who defies your power and mine. Quick! Take up your darts! Send an arrow into the breast of that dark monarch. Let him, too, feel the pangs of love. Why should he alone escape them?"

At his mother's words, Eros leaped lightly to his feet. He chose from his quiver his sharpest and truest arrow, fitted it to his bow, drew the string, and shot straight into Pluto's heart.

The grim King had seen fair maids enough in the gloomy underworld over which he ruled. But never had his heart been touched. Now an unaccustomed warmth stole through his veins. His stern eyes softened. Before him was a blossoming valley, and along its edge a charming girl was gathering flowers. She was Persephone, daughter of Demeter, goddess of the harvest. She had strayed from her companions, and now that her basket overflowed with blossoms, she was filling her apron with lilies and violets. The god looked at Persephone and loved her at once. With one sweep of his arm he caught her up and drove swiftly away.

"Mother!" she screamed, while the flowers

fell from her apron and strewed the ground. "Mother!"

And she called on her companions by name. But already they were out of sight, so fast did Pluto urge the horses on. In a few moments they were at the River Cyane. Persephone struggled, her loosened girdle fell to the ground, but the god held her tight. He struck the bank with his trident. The earth opened, and darkness swallowed them all—horses, chariot, Pluto, and weeping Persephone.

From end to end of the earth Demeter sought her daughter. But none could tell her where Persephone was. At last, worn out and despairing, the goddess returned to Sicily. She stood by the River Cyane, where Pluto had cleft the earth and gone down into his own dominions.

Now a river nymph had seen him carry off his prize. She wanted to tell Demeter where her daughter was, but fear of Pluto kept her dumb. Yet she had picked up the girdle Persephone had dropped, and this the nymph wafted on the waves to the feet of Demeter.

The goddess knew then that her daughter was gone indeed, but she did not suspect Pluto of carrying her off. She laid the blame on the innocent land.

"Ungrateful soil!" she said. "I made you fertile. I clothed you in grass and nourishing grain, and this is how you reward me. No more shall you enjoy my favors!"

That year was the most cruel mankind had ever known. Nothing prospered, nothing grew. The cattle died, the seed would not come up, men and oxen toiled in vain. There was too much sun. There was too much rain. Thistles and weeds were the only things that grew. It seemed that all mankind would die of hunger.

was to be preserved. So he called Hermes to him and said:

"Descend to the underworld, my son. Bid Pluto release his bride. Provided she has not tasted food in the realm of the dead, she may return to her mother forever."

Down sped Hermes on his winged feet, and there in the dim palace of the king, he found Persephone by Pluto's side. She was pale and joyless. Not all the glittering treasures of the underworld could bring a smile to her lips.

"You have no flowers here," she would say to her husband when he pressed gems upon her. "Jewels have no fragrance. I do not want them."

When she saw Hermes and heard his message, her heart leaped within her. Her cheeks grew rosy and her eyes sparkled, for she knew that Pluto would not dare to disobey his brother's command. She sprang up, ready to go at once. Only one thing troubled her— that she could not leave the underworld forever. For she had accepted a pomegranate from Pluto and sucked the sweet pulp from four of the seeds.

With a heavy heart Pluto made ready his golden car. He helped Persephone in while Hermes took up the reins.

"Dear wife," said the King, and his voice trembled as he spoke, "think kindly of me, I pray you. For indeed I love you truly. It will be lonely here these eight months you are away. And if you think mine is a gloomy palace to return to, at least remember that your husband is great among the immortals. So fare you well—and get your fill of flowers!"

Straight to the temple of Demeter at Eleusis, Hermes drove the black horses. The goddess heard the chariot wheels and, as a deer bounds over the hills, she ran out swiftly to meet her daughter. Persephone flew to her mother's arms. And the sad tale of each turned into joy in the telling.

So it is to this day. One third of the year Persephone spends in the gloomy abode of Pluto—one month for each seed that she tasted. Then Nature dies, the leaves fall, the earth stops bringing forth. In spring Persephone returns, and with her come the flowers, followed by summer's fruitfulness and the rich harvest of fall.

"This cannot go on," said mighty Zeus. "I see that I must intervene." And one by one he sent the gods and goddesses to plead with Demeter.

But she had the same answer for all: "Not till I see my daughter shall the earth bear fruit again."

Zeus, of course, knew well where Persephone was. He did not like to take from his brother the one joyful thing in his life, but he saw that he must if the race of man

ECHO AN|

O F ALL the mountain nymphs, none was more charming than Echo. But she had one fault. She talked too much. It was chatter, chatter all day long, and no matter what the subject, Echo always had the last word.

Now one day when Zeus was enjoying the company of the nymphs, Hera suddenly appeared. All hurried to get away except Echo, who, to distract the goddess, started to talk. She kept Hera amused so long that the nymphs made their escape. But Hera was furious when she found out how she had been deceived.

"You shall never get the chance to do it again," she told Echo. "That amusing tongue of yours shall lose its power. From now on it will never be able to start chattering, nor do anything except the one thing you are so fond of—reply. Yes, indeed, you shall have the last word, Echo. But that is all you will have! Never will you be able to speak *first!*"

Soon after this, Echo found out just how bad her punishment was. She fell in love, and, as luck would have it, with a young hunter who could not love anybody but himself. Narcissus was an exceptionally handsome youth. But he was as cold as he was handsome.

Poor Echo trailed all over the mountains after Narcissus. How she longed to speak to him and win his love by gentle words! Alas, she had not the power!

Then one day while Narcissus was hunting, it happened that he became separated from his companions.

"Who's here?" he shouted.

"Here!" Echo replied.

NARCISSUS

Narcissus looked around. He could see no one.

"Come!" he called.

Echo immediately answered, "Come!"

Narcissus waited, but when no one came, he called again: "Why do you keep away from me?"

"Away from me!" Echo called back.

"Let us meet!" Narcissus said.

"Let us meet!" the nymph agreed with all her heart. She ran to the spot, arms upraised and ready to throw around his neck.

Narcissus started back. "Do not touch me!" he cried. "I would rather die than that you should have me!"

"Have me!" Echo pleaded.

But in vain. The young man strode off, leaving the nymph to hide her blushes in the thick woods.

From that time on, Echo would never show herself. Caves and mountain cliffs became her home. Her body wasted away with grief and longing until all her flesh was gone. Her bones changed into rocks. And nothing was left of her but her voice, with which she still replies to anyone who calls.

Cruel Narcissus! Echo was not the only being whose heart he broke. But at last he got what he deserved. A maiden whom he had spurned asked the goddess of vengeance to take her part.

"Oh, may the time come," the girl prayed, "when Narcissus may feel what it is to love and get no love in return!"

And the avenging goddess heard. . . .

There was a sparkling spring in the hills, to which for some reason shepherds never drove their flocks. Neither did mountain goats nor any beasts of the forest ever drink from it. Fresh green grass grew all around, and rocks sheltered the spring from the sun. The water in the pool was as clear as polished silver. Not a dead branch, not a dead leaf polluted it.

To this pool one day Narcissus came, worn out with hunting, hot and thirsty. He stooped down to drink—and saw his lovely image in the water.

"It is the water-spirit," he thought, for he had never seen his own reflection before. Enchanted, he knelt down to look and could not take his gaze away. He bent close to place a kiss upon the parted lips, and stretched out his arms to clasp the lovely being. At his touch the image dissolved into a thousand ripples. But even as he watched, it came back as clear as before.

"Beautiful being," Narcissus said, "why do you flee from me? Surely my face cannot displease you, for every nymph of the mountains is in love with me, and you yourself look as if you are not indifferent. Your smile answers mine. When I stretch out my arms to you, you do the same."

Tears of longing rolled down his cheeks and splashed into the silver pool. At once the image fled again.

"Stay, oh, stay!" he pleaded. "If I may not touch you, let me at least gaze upon you!"

He was unable to tear himself away. Day after day he hung over the water, feasting his eyes on his own reflection. Love, which he had so often scorned, now so consumed him that he lost his color and was no more than a waxy image of himself. All he could do was sigh, "Alas! Alas!" And Echo answered him, "Alas!"

At last Narcissus faded away altogether and passed from the upper world. But even as his shade was being ferried to the regions of the dead, it looked down into the river Styx to catch a last beloved reflection. The nymphs who had given their hearts to him heaped wood into a funeral pile and would have burned his body, as the custom was. But his remains were nowhere to be found. Only a wax-white flower with a purple heart stood in the place where he had knelt and sighed. And to this flower the grieving maidens gave his name—Narcissus.

ORPHEUS

IN THE kingdom of Thrace there lived a poet and sweet singer, Orpheus by name. His father, who was Apollo, had given him a lyre and taught him to play it. So it is no wonder that the young man's music charmed everyone. So enchanting was it, indeed, that when Orpheus plucked the strings, wild beasts gathered round him and grew tame. He drew the very trees after him. The rocks on the hillsides moved to his music, and the rivers changed their courses that they might hear him.

Many maidens loved Orpheus, yet he loved one alone—Eurydice. And one day they were married. But while the young bride wandered with her bridesmaids in a meadow, a serpent bit her ankle and she fell lifeless to the ground.

Who can describe the grief of Orpheus then? Day and night he wept for his lost wife. But tears brought no ease to his spirit.

AND EURYDICE

His heart grew heavier instead of lighter, and at last he determined to do what no other mortal man had dared do for his love before. He would descend to the underworld and beg Pluto to restore Eurydice.

Now Orpheus knew where a deep cavern led far into the earth, and by means of it he got down to the river Styx.

"Take me across!" Orpheus said to Pluto's ferryman.

"No," Charon answered, "my bark is made for the shades of the dead. You are too heavy. I dare not take you."

But when Orpheus struck his lyre, the ferryman yielded. Cerberus, the three-headed dog who guarded the entrance to Pluto's realm, would not let him by. But he yielded too when Orpheus played his lyre. So the poet entered the realm of the dead, passed among the shades, and came to the throne of Pluto and Persephone.

He bowed low before the King and Queen. Then he plucked the strings of his lyre, and accompanying his words with tenderest music, began to sing:

"O Lords of the Underworld! I do not come here to spy out the secrets of your realm. I come to seek my wife, cut off in her bloom when she trod on a serpent and it poured its poison in her veins. I have tried to endure my grief, but I cannot—Love is too much for me. Love led me here—Love, a god well known to us who dwell on earth. And here, too, he is familiar if the story of yourselves is true.

"For you, too, O King and Queen, were brought together by Love. I implore you, by these haunts of terror, by these realms of silence, make whole again the thread of Eurydice's life. All of us mortals must descend to you at last. For this is our final home, and yours is the most lasting sway

over mankind. My wife, like all the rest, will come within your power in time. But until then, I implore you, grant her to me. If you refuse, keep me here, too. I do not wish to return alone. Triumph in my death as well as hers."

He sang, and as the sweet music and moving words swept through the dismal halls, the bloodless shades shed tears. The very instruments of punishment ceased from inflicting pain, and all the doomed rested from their weary tasks. Then for the first time the cheeks of the pitiless Furies were wet with tears. Wet, too, were the eyes of Persephone. And even Pluto softened, as on that day when Eros shot the arrow into his heart. Iron tears rolled down his cheeks.

"Let Eurydice be called!" he said.

"Eurydice! Eurydice!" sounded through the silent halls of death. And out of the depths where all the newly-arrived shades flocked together, pale Eurydice came, walking slowly because of her injured foot. She stood sadly before the throne, not knowing why she was being summoned. And then she saw Orpheus and her shadowy face lit up with such joy as those regions had never beheld.

"Take her," Pluto said. "But remember! Do not look back until you have reached the upper air. For if you do, Eurydice will die again."

Through gloom and heavy silence Orpheus passed first up the steep, dark, narrow, sloping path, and Eurydice came limping behind. Joy filled the poet's heart. His daring had succeeded. His music had made the grim god grant what love demanded. If only Eurydice's strength would not fail her till they reached the surface!

Near the top it suddenly seemed to Orpheus that he could no longer hear Eurydice's step behind him. Seized with panic, he turned to see if she was there. And at once Eurydice slipped back into the depths.

"Come to me, my love, come back!" Orpheus cried, stretching out his arms. "Do not die a second time and leave me desolate!"

But no answer came from the gloom. For a long time Orpheus stood staring into nothingness, then, turning, he went his heavy upward way.

THE GORGON'S HEAD
PERSEUS GOES ON A QUEST

CRISIUS, King of Argos, came home from Delphi with a heavy heart, for he had received a dreadful oracle.

"No sons shall be born to you," the priestess had told him. "But you shall have a grandson, and by his hand you shall die."

Now the king had an only daughter, who was yet a maiden. So in his distress he thought: "I will evade my fate. I will shut Danae up away from the sight of men in a house of bronze all sunk underground." And he carried out his cruel plan.

But Acrisius forgot to take the gods into account. Part of the roof of the house was open to the sky. And one day, as lovely Danae sat sadly looking up at the passing clouds, Zeus beheld the maiden. Changing himself into a shower of gold, he stormed into her chamber.

When afterwards a son was born to Danae, she hid him from her father's sight. Nevertheless, the king discovered the baby and was more than ever filled with fear. He dared not kill the little Perseus directly lest the gods avenge the murder. Instead, he had a great chest built, placed Danae and her boy in it, and set them adrift upon the sea.

All day and all night the chest tossed upon

the waves. Danae lulled her child with song, and he slept. But when dawn came, a great wave picked up the chest and carried it close to the tiny island of Seraphos.

It happened that a fisherman, Dictys by name, saw the chest bobbing on the waves close to the shore. He dragged the box to land and opened it. When he beheld the pitiful mother with the helpless little child, his heart was moved. He took them both to his wife, for Dictys was childless, and there in the kindly fisherfolk's humble home Perseus grew up.

Now Danae had been a beautiful maiden. And when Perseus was grown into a fine tall youth, she was still beautiful. So it was not strange that King Polydectes, who was Dictys' brother, fell in love with her and made her his wife. But the King hated the youth—just because Danae doted on him—and sought some way to be rid of him.

At last Polydectes said to his stepson, "The time has come, Perseus, for you to win glory for yourself in some bold adventure."

Young Perseus thought so, too. But what should the adventure be?

"I think," the wily Polydectes said, "it would be a good idea for you to cut off the Medusa's head. That would bring you the greatest fame."

All unsuspecting, Perseus set off to find the Medusa, not knowing in the least how perilous an adventure he had undertaken. For the Medusa was one of the three Gorgons, terrible winged monsters who lived alone on an island. They had teeth like the tusks of a boar, hands of brass, and snakes instead of hair. Perseus did not know where to look for the Gorgons. Nor did he know which of them was Medusa. And this was important, for Medusa was the only one of the three that could be slain.

From place to place the prince went in his quest, getting more and more discouraged. Then one day he beheld a young man of great beauty, wearing winged sandals and a winged cap, and carrying in his hand a wand around which two golden serpents twined. Perseus knew at once that this was Hermes and was overjoyed when the god said:

"Perseus, I approve the high adventure you have in mind. But you must be properly equipped for it. Without the winged sandals, the magic wallet, and the helmet of invisibility which the Nymphs of the North possess, you can never succeed. Now, I cannot tell you where the Nymphs live, but I will take you to the Gray Women. You can find out from them."

"And will they indeed tell me?" Perseus asked.

"Not willingly," Hermes replied. "But you can make them do it. They have but one eye among the three. Snatch it from them as they pass it from one to another and none can see. And do not give it back till they tell you what you want to know."

With that, Hermes gave Perseus a magnificent curved sword.

"You will need it," he said, "for the Medusa's scales are hard as metal."

Perseus had just taken the sword when there was a sudden brightness in the sky, and he beheld the goddess Athene descending toward them.

"Of what use will be your sword, my brother," she said to Hermes, "when none may look on the Gorgons and live? The sight of them, as you well know, turns men to stone. Take my bright shield, Perseus. Look into it instead of at the monster as you approach to do battle, and you will see the Medusa reflected as in a mirror."

So saying, the goddess disappeared, and the brightness with her.

On and on with his god-companion Perseus journeyed, farther than man had ever been. At last they came to the end of the earth. There the weird Gray Women sat, passing their eye from one to another just as Hermes had said. Danae's son knew what to do. He left the god and crept quietly towards them, waited till one had taken the eye from her forehead, and snatched it away as she passed it to her sister.

The Gray Women raised a fearful clamor when they realized that a stranger had their eye. They howled and they threatened. But without their eye they were helpless, and in the end they grudgingly told Perseus the way to the Nymphs of the North.

So again Perseus went on, this time to find

the happy beings who possessed the three priceless things he needed. And when the Nymphs heard the reason he wanted them, they were willing to give him the winged shoes, the helmet that would make him invisible, and the magic wallet that would become the right size for whatever he wished to carry.

Fully equipped now, Perseus lightly sped through the air over land and over sea to the fearful island of the Gorgons. As he approached, he could see, scattered in the fields and along the roads, statues of men and beasts whom the sight of the Gorgons had turned to stone. And, at last, from high above, he beheld the monsters themselves reflected in his shield. Their scale-covered bodies glistened in the sun, their great wings were folded, the snakes that were their hair

lay hideously coiled and intertwined. The Gorgons were asleep.

But which of the three was Medusa? Perseus could see no difference between them.

Suddenly he heard Athene's voice:

"Descend, Perseus, and strike! The Gorgon nearest the shore is Medusa."

Perseus swept down, and still gazing into the shield, boldly swung his blade. With one stroke he cut off the grisly head. Then, springing into the air, he thrust his prize, all writhing and hissing, into the magic wallet.

Up leaped the Gorgon sisters, for they heard the rattle of Medusa's scales as the severed body thrashed about. They turned their snaky heads and when they saw Perseus, they roared with fury. Flapping their great wings, they set off in pursuit. But they could not outstrip the winged sandals.

29

ANDROMEDA

OVER LANDS and peoples the hero flew, on and on. He had lost his way now, for Hermes had left him. Below, the Lybian desert stretched endlessly. Perseus did not know what those sands were, nor did he guess that the ruby drops falling from Medusa's head were turning into venomous snakes that would inhabit the desert forever. But now he saw a sight that made his heart beat fast with excitement and wonder.

Fastened by chains to a cliff by the sea was a beautiful maiden. Had it not been that a slight breeze stirred her hair and that tears flowed from her eyes, he would have thought her a statue. Perseus almost forgot to keep his winged sandals moving, so struck was he by her rare beauty.

"Lovely maiden, you should not wear such chains as these," he stammered out, "but rather those which bind the hearts of lovers. I pray you, tell me your name and why you are bound like this."

At first the girl made no reply, so abashed was she before the youth. But when he urged her again and again to speak, she told him all her story.

"I am Andromeda," she said, "daughter of Cepheus, King of the Ethiopians. The beautiful Cassiopeia is my mother. It is her beauty that has chained me here. For the gods are jealous, and in nothing may we mortals surpass them. Woe, woe the day my mother vaunted herself fairer than the daughters of Nereus! The sea god has sent a serpent to prey upon our people, and my death alone can appease his anger. So says the oracle."

She had scarcely finished speaking when the loud roaring of the waves announced that the monster was on his way. Andromeda shrieked. At her cry, her frantic father and mother came running. They clung to their daughter and lamented.

"Enough of tears!" Perseus said to them sternly. "I am Perseus, son of Zeus and Danae. Now I will make this contract with you—that Andromeda shall be mine if I save her from the serpent."

"Indeed, indeed, valorous youth, she shall be yours! Only save her from the monster, and you shall have our kingdom as well as our daughter."

The monster was coming on, his breast parting the waves like a swift ship. Suddenly Perseus sprang into the air and shot high up in the clouds. Seeing the youth's shadow upon the sea, the monster attacked it in fury. Then Perseus swooped like an eagle from the sky and buried his sword up to the hilt in the beast's right shoulder. The creature reared upright, then plunged beneath the water, and turned around and around like some fierce wild boar in the midst of baying hounds.

Nimbly avoiding the snapping jaws, Perseus dealt blow after blow wherever he had the chance to strike. Red blood poured from the monster's mouth. The air was so filled with spray that the hero's winged sandals grew heavy. He dared not trust himself to them longer. Spying a rock over which the waves were breaking, he braced himself against it with his left hand, and four times he drove his sword into the monster's side.

As the creature sank to its death, Perseus heard shouts of joy from the shore. And when he looked, Andromeda already stood free beside her parents.

"I will take this fair maiden without dowry," Perseus said.

And that very day the wedding was celebrated. Torches were tossed in the air, incense was thrown on the flames. Garlands were hung from the palace roof. And everywhere the sound of lyres and pipes and singing was heard.

MEN BECOME STONE

Now while the marriage feast was at its height, the door of the banquet hall was suddenly flung open, and in burst a mob of shouting, riotous men. Foremost stood Andromeda's uncle, Phineas, javelin in hand.

"Behold, I am here!" he cried. "I have come to avenge the theft of my promised bride."

"What are you doing, brother?" the father cried. "Do you, who stood by and watched while Andromeda was put in chains and did nothing to help her, dare to be indignant because another has snatched the prize? Let the man who rescued her have the reward he was promised! He has not been chosen in preference to you, but in preference to certain death."

Phineas said not a word. He looked from the king to Perseus, undecided at which to aim his weapon, then hurled it at the hero. The spear struck in Perseus' couch.

Perseus leaped up from the cushions, wrenched out the spear, and hurled it back at his foe. Had Phineas not taken refuge behind the altar, he would have perished. As it was, one of his followers received the weapon full in his forehead.

Then the rioters went wild. Weapons were hurled, and the feast turned into a battle. Thick as hail, javelins sped by Perseus' ears. He set his shoulders against a great stone column and struck down one man after another. But at last he realized that valor could not withstand the numbers against him.

"If I have any friends here, let them hide their faces!" he shouted.

With this he drew Medusa's head out of the wallet. One of the attackers was just preparing to cast his javelin, but before he could cast, he was turned to stone. Another, who was about to thrust his sword through Perseus, stood frozen with it in his hand. A third was turned to stone even as he uttered a taunt. Two hundred men became stony statues before Phineas yielded, crying:

"Put away your horrible weapon. Hide it! Grant me only my life and may the rest be yours!"

"What I can give you, most cowardly Phineas, I will!" Perseus replied. "You shall be a lasting monument here in the palace of my father-in-law."

The unhappy Phineas tried to turn away his eyes, but even as he did so, his flesh turned to stone.

THE ORACLE IS FULFILLED

WHEN at the year's end, Perseus sailed home with Andromeda, Polydectes' hatred had in no way lessened. The King was furious that his stepson had returned, and refused to believe that he had actually slain the Medusa. With scornful taunts he upbraided the young man for having come home empty-handed.

It was more than Perseus could bear.

"I shall prove to you that what I say is true!" he cried. "Hide your eyes, all you who are my friends!" And he showed the Gorgon's head to cruel Polydectes.

That was the last time Perseus ever used the horrible head. He gave it most willingly to Athene, who kept it ever after.

Now that Polydectes was dead, Danae yearned to go home again and be reconciled to her father. So Perseus made the fisherman Dictys king of the island and sailed with his mother and Andromeda to Greece.

But it happened that when they came to Argos, King Acrisius was away from home. Games were being held in Larissa, and Perseus, hearing of them, decided to go there and take part. And there at the games it was that the oracle which Acrisius had received at Delphi was strangely fulfilled. For when it came Perseus' turn to throw the discus, he threw it so that it swerved to one side. It landed among the spectators and killed an old man. That old man was King Acrisius, who had gone to such cruel lengths to avoid the fate which the gods had ordained.

HERACLES

THE TWELVE LABORS

O F ALL the heroes of Greece, the mightiest was the son of Zeus and Alcmene, granddaughter of Perseus. Zeus called him Heracles, *Glory of Hera*. The compliment, however, did not soften the jealous heart of Hera, the queen of heaven. She hated her namesake and sent two serpents to strangle the baby in his cradle. But Heracles awoke when he felt the coils about his throat, seized the serpents by their necks, and squeezed until the life went out of them.

From that time on, great things were expected of the marvelous child. So Alcmene's husband, King Amphitrion, had him carefully educated in the arts of war and boxing and wrestling. The boy learned quickly, and at eighteen he was the strongest and handsomest youth in Greece. He yearned to be a hero, to serve his country, to win a glorious name for himself. So he set about fighting with wild beasts and giants. And it was not long before his prowess was known up and down the land.

Now, before Heracles was born, Hera had made Zeus promise her that the first prince born to the House of Perseus should be High King and rule over Perseus' other descendants. Zeus had consented to this because he expected that Heracles would be the one born first. But Hera contrived to have Eurystheus come into the world an hour ahead of Heracles. And thus Eurystheus became King of Mycenae and Heracles was forced to be his subject.

However, the hero was much more famous than the King, and this did not please Eurystheus at all.

"I will set him dangerous labors to perform," he said to himself. "In one or another of them he will surely lose his life." And he summoned Heracles and bade him slay the lion of Nemea, a fearful beast that could not be killed by weapons of war.

Heracles refused to do it. "It is not fitting that I, a demigod, should be your servant," he said.

At this point Zeus intervened. "You must obey, my son," he said. "Eurystheus is King."

35

So Heracles submitted, and went out and strangled the Nemean lion with his bare hands. Ever after he wore its jaws for a helmet and its skin for a cloak.

Then at Eurystheus' command he slew the nine-headed Hydra, a huge water snake that crept out of the Lernean marshes to tear cattle limb from limb.

He took alive the hind of Mount Cerynea. For a full year Heracles followed this swift and delicate creature with golden horns and brazen hoofs. But he lamed and took it at last and carried it through Arcadia on his shoulders.

He also caught alive the fierce Erymanthean Boar that ravaged the country round about.

When Heracles set this enormous creature, sacred to Artemis, unharmed before Eurystheus, the king despaired. "No feat of strength is beyond this fellow," he thought, "and each brings him greater fame. I will set him some task beneath a hero's dignity, yet one he is bound to fail in."

And so he said to Heracles, "The stables of Augeas, King of Elis, are foul. Pestilence spreads from them even to the gates of Mycenae. Go you to Elis and cleanse that cattle-yard. And see that the task is done between the rise and set of sun."

Now King Augeas had three thousand head of cattle in an enclosure in front of the palace. They had been living there many years, and the stables had never been cleaned. But Heracles accomplished this labor, too, and in a manner that added mightily to his fame. He cut two holes in the cattle-yard wall. Then he turned the course of two neighboring rivers so that they rushed through the yard and washed the filth away.

After that Eurystheus thought of the Stymphalian birds. The flocks of these ravenous birds with wings and beaks and claws of iron were so enormous that it seemed impossible Heracles could destroy them. But Heracles terrified the birds with rattles, and when they flew up killed so many of them with arrows that the rest abandoned the land.

Then Heracles traveled to Crete and brought to Eurystheus the wild bull of Poseidon. He also tamed the mares of Diomedes of Thrace that fed on human flesh.

He fought with the Amazons and took to Eurystheus the girdle of their queen. He killed the three-bodied giant Geryon and carried off his oxen.

By this time Eurystheus had all but lost hope. Heracles had now performed ten labors for him. From each the hero had risen stronger and more renowned. Still the King would not give up. He demanded that Heracles fetch him the golden apples of the Hesperides.

Now these apples grew in a sacred garden, none knew where, and were watched over by an unsleeping, hundred-headed dragon and also by the daughters of Night, whom men called the Hesperides. Heracles had no idea where to find the sacred garden. But he set off, and in his wandering came to the Caucasus. There, high on the peak of a mountain, he saw Prometheus bound. He set the Titan free. And Prometheus told him how to find the sacred garden.

"You will find it where Atlas stands holding the vault of heaven on his shoulders. But do not try to get the golden apples yourself. My brother Atlas is the father of the Hesperides. Persuade him to get the apples for you."

At last the hero arrived in that part of the world where the mighty Titan stood holding up the sky.

"I will take your burden on my shoulders and give you a rest," Heracles said, "if you will get me some of the golden apples from the garden of the Hesperides."

Atlas readily agreed, and lulling the dragon to sleep, brought Heracles three of the golden apples. But the Titan had tasted freedom and it seemed good to him.

"I had forgotten what it felt like to have nothing resting on my shoulders," he said to Heracles. "Now you can hold up the sky." And he walked away.

"Wait, Atlas!" Heracles cried. He was thinking faster than he had ever done before, for he saw that strength would not help him now. Only guile would do. "Wait! I am willing to take your place. But hold the sky a minute till I coil a rope around my head. Otherwise the weight will crush me."

The stupid Titan did as Heracles asked—and the hero promptly went on his way, leaving Atlas as he was before.

When Heracles laid the golden apples before Eurystheus, the king realized that no labor under the sun was beyond the hero. Still he thought, "Surely the powers of the underworld will prove too much for Heracles. I will send him to Hades to bring me the three-headed dog, Cerberus, that guards the gate to the kingdom of the shades."

But Heracles performed this twelfth labor as nobly as the others. Then at last Eurystheus saw that it was useless. All he had accomplished by setting up labors for Heracles was to build his renown. So he bade him take Cerberus back to Hades, and from then on troubled the hero no more.

DEIANIRA AND THE CENTAUR

ALTHOUGH all Greece knew of his prowess, Heracles did not cease from doing bold deeds. Year by year he kept adding to his glory. For neither men, nor beasts, nor giants, nor gods could get the better of this wonderful demigod.

Now in his travels the hero came one day to Calydon, where he wooed and won the king's beautiful daughter, Deianira. Afterwards he took her to his native city. And on the journey there he had a strange adventure.

The winter rains had swollen the river Euenas, which they had to cross. Heracles looked at the swirling eddies. For himself he had no fear, but how was he to get Deianira across? As he stood, wondering what to do, the centaur Nessus, who knew the fords well, ambled up.

"I will take your wife on my back," he said, "and set her on the other side. Keep your strength for swimming."

"Agreed," Heracles replied, and helped Deianira to mount. Then he threw his club and his bow across the river and plunged in just as he was, weighed down by his quiver and lion skin.

He had reached the other bank and was picking up his bow when he heard his wife cry out. The centaur—who had crossed before him—was making off with Deianira.

"Villain!" Heracles cried. "Where are you off to? Do not think to come between me and mine. Though you have horse's hoofs, you will not escape me, for I will overtake you with my deadly arrows!"

As he said this, Heracles bent his bow and loosed a shaft. It pierced deeply into the centaur's back and the barbed point protruded from his breast.

Nessus knew that his time on earth was done, for the arrows of Heracles had been dipped in the poisonous blood of the nine-headed Hydra.

"But I shall not die unavenged," he thought. And aloud he said, "O daughter of Oeneus! I am dying, and I would serve you because you are the last to ride upon my back. Take up the clotted blood at the point where the arrow entered my body. It has a magic in it. If you dye your husband's shirt with it, he will never love any woman more than you."

With that he sank down and breathed his last. Deianira did not doubt her husband's love. Nevertheless, she took out a vial she had by her and quickly did as the centaur had bade her.

"Who knows what may not come to pass?" she thought. And she kept the vial hidden from Heracles.

NESSUS HAS HIS REVENGE

YEARS went by, many years that for Heracles were filled with glory. Deianira had forgotten all about the vial containing what she supposed was a charm, when one day she found occasion to use it.

Heracles had gone on an expedition against King Eurytus, against whom he bore a grudge. Long ago this king had refused to give him his daughter Iole, with whom Heracles had been in love. The hero now had his revenge. He slew the king and his three sons and took the still beautiful Iole captive. On his way home he stopped to make a sacrifice of thanksgiving for his victory, but he sent all his captives on with his servant Lichas.

Deianira saw the beautiful Iole and her heart was filled with pity for the captive. But when she heard it was on account of Iole that Heracles had gone on this expedition and destroyed King Eurytus, her pity was turned on herself. She did not know what course to take. Then she remembered the charm she had so long hidden. Quickly she took a sacrificial shirt which she had woven, dipped a tuft of wool in the blood, and dyed the garment. Then she folded it into a chest and called Lichas.

"Take this sacrificial shirt to my husband," she said. "Be careful not to expose it to light or heat until Heracles is about to wear it."

Lichas had not long driven away in the chariot when Deianira returned to her chamber. On the floor lay the tuft of wool she had used in dyeing. She looked at it aghast. It was burning away like sawdust, and red foam bubbled all around it.

"Oh, cursed folly!" she cried. "The centaur deceived me! I swear to you, O gods, that if I have caused Heracles to die, I shall not survive him." And she sent a man to stop Lichas.

But it was too late. By the time the courier arrived, Heracles had already put on the shirt and he was performing the sacrifice. Twelve perfect bulls and a hundred head of mixed cattle had been slaughtered. Heracles was pouring wine upon the marble altars and throwing incense on the flames.

Suddenly he cried out, as if a serpent had stung him. For the poison, melted by the fire, was beginning to work. He tried to rip off the shirt, but it clung to his body, and wherever he was able to tear the cloth away, it pulled skin and flesh with it, revealing his bones. His blood hissed and boiled. Dark perspiration poured from him, and his scorched sinews crackled. Overthrowing the altars, he ran and plunged into the nearest stream, but the poison burned only the more. Raging, he ran about tearing up trees or rolling in agony upon the ground.

"O Hera," he cried, raising his eyes to the heavens, "even your barbarous heart must be satisfied when you see my torment! Was it for this that I faced the triple-bodied Geryon and the dog Cerberus? Are these the hands that forced down the horns of the mighty Cretan bull, that won the girdle of the Amazon queen, that brought home the golden apples of the Hesperides? The boar that ravaged Arcadia could not resist me, nor the nine-headed Lernean Hydra. The Thracian horses that fed on human flesh are destroyed. The lion of Nemea lies dead,

throttled by these hands. I have held the sky upon my shoulders. But now a plague is upon me which no amount of courage nor any weapons of war can overcome. Fire consumes my flesh and eats into my lungs. My enemy King Eurystheus, for whom I toiled in mighty labors, is strong and well! And yet there are men who believe the gods are just!"

Crying out like some wounded wild bull that carries a hunting spear in his body, Heracles raged over the land. All at once he saw Lichas, pale and terrified, hiding in a cave.

"Was it you who brought me this deadly gift?" the hero cried.

In vain Lichas tried to embrace his master's knees. Heracles seized him in his arms, swung him three, four times around, and flung him, as a stone is shot from a sling, into the Euboean Sea.

And still the poison raged and still Heracles suffered and could not die, so strong was he. They brought him home. Deianira had taken her life.

Then Heracles ordered trees to be cut down and a pyre built. His young friend and follower Philoctetes kindled the pyre. As the flames licked the wood, Heracles put the skin of the Nemean lion on top of the pile and lay down upon it. He seemed like one who lies on a couch at a banquet.

Even the gods were dismayed as the flames rose up around Heracles. But Zeus calmed their fears.

"Heracles, who has conquered all, will conquer the fire, too," he said. "Only the human part of him that he got from his mother Alcmene will be consumed. What he has received from me is immortal. I shall take him into the realms of heaven. For this is what he deserves."

The gods applauded, and even Hera kept her silence.

Meantime all of Heracles that fire could ravage had burned away, and yet the form of the hero was left, showing all his likeness to his father. Those who watched saw a cloud descend. In its midst stood Zeus in his chariot. He stretched out his hand, swept up the hero, and set him among the stars.

THE GOLDEN FLEECE

THE MAN WITH ONE SANDAL

Jason was the rightful heir to the throne of Iolcus, but there seemed little chance that he would ever sit upon it. For his uncle Pelias had seized it and driven Jason's father away. The boy himself had been brought up by the centaur Chiron. This kindly creature, who was half-horse, half-man, had educated many heroes in his cave.

Under his care Jason learned all that befits a stalwart man to know.

Now Pelias, the false king, was troubled by a strange oracle. He had been told to beware of a man wearing but one sandal. Pelias turned the mysterious words over and over in his mind, but could make nothing of them. And he was still worrying about the meaning years later, when Jason, his nephew, decided to travel to Iolcus and assert his rights.

Jason had grown into a tall, handsome man, and as he journeyed along, none could help admiring him. His bright, unshorn locks hung down his neck. The skin of a leopard he had strangled was thrown over his close-fitting leather tunic. Two broad-bladed spears were in his hand. He looked so much like a god that many he met wondered whether he might not be one of the immortals.

As he approached the city of Iolcus, Jason had to cross a muddy river, and in crossing it he lost his sandal in the mud. So he arrived in the market place of the capital wearing but one. The place was thronged, for the King was just then making a sacrifice.

"Who can that be?" the people said to one another, looking at the handsome stranger with wonder. "Is this perhaps Apollo come in disguise?"

But the King's eyes went—as ever they did—to the stranger's feet. He saw but one sandal, and his face paled and his heart all but stood still.

"Who are you and what is your father's name?" the King asked when the rites were finished.

"I am Jason, the son of King Aeson," the young man replied. "And I have come to visit my father's house."

Pelias hid his fears under courteous words and invited Jason into the palace, where he entertained his nephew royally for five days. Then Jason said to him in a matter-of-fact way:

"This kingdom is mine for I am the rightful heir. But I shall leave you the wealth you took from my father. All the fields and the herds shall be yours. I ask only the sceptre and throne which were my father's."

Pelias thought fast, and his face changed color several times as he spoke.

"All shall be as you wish," he said. "But I, too, have a request to make. I have been troubled by a dream. The shade of Phrixus has appeared to me. He has implored me to bring back to Greece the golden fleece of that sacred ram which once carried him across the sea to Colchis and which afterwards he sacrificed to Zeus. Go you in my stead. Bring back to Greece that glorious prize and put the spirit of Phrixus at rest."

When Jason heard these words, his soul was mightily stirred. For the golden fleece was the great prize of which every hero in Greece dreamed. All knew that in the land of Colchis the golden fleece hung from an oak in a sacred grove, where an unsleeping dragon guarded it by day and by night. Jason's mind and heart were instantly so filled with longing for it that he did not stop to examine his wily uncle's reasons for proposing the adventure to him.

"I will go to Colchis with a band of heroes," he agreed at once. "And I will set the soul of Phrixus at ease."

Thereupon Jason sent heralds to all the courts of Greece, calling for bold men who dared to sail with him. And he had Argus the Thespian build him a fifty-oared ship.

Hero after hero answered the call. Argus himself volunteered to go, he who had built the vessel. Heracles of Tiryns, the strongest man who ever lived, joined Jason. Laertes, grandson of Zeus, who one day would be father of Odysseus of the many adventures, came from Argos. Orpheus, the poet and wondrous musician who descended into Hades to seek his dead wife, Eurydice, hastened from Thrace. Peleus, who would one day father Achilles, the great hero of the Trojan War, also came. And many others of glittering fame hastened to Iolcus, so that never before had so gallant a ship's company come together.

When all was ready, Jason made a solemn offering to the gods of the sea. The heroes took their seats at the oars, and the *Argo* weighed anchor. Dangers untold lay before the bold Argonauts. But not one of the heroes lost heart.

were and what their errand was than his manner changed.

"Not for the golden fleece but to take my sceptre and my throne you have come!" he broke out in fury. "Return to your homes before I have your tongues cut out and your hands lopped off!"

"Restrain your anger, King Aeetes," Jason answered courteously. "We have come for no other purpose than I have stated. Destiny and the command of a wicked king prompted me to come. I pray you, grant our request. Give us the golden fleece. And if there is any service we can render you as fighting men, we shall gladly do it."

The King frowned. Then, changing his manner, he spoke more mildly.

JASON'S TASK

WHO can tell of all that happened before the Argonauts reached Colchis? It would take many books to say the whole, for countless men have recorded the adventures of the heroes, and each tells the story in his own way. But arrive at last they did. It was sunset, and they were weary. They took down their sails, then rowed up the river toward the capital, and made the vessel fast. With a grateful heart, Jason offered up a libation to the gods. Then, filled with uncertainty about the morrow, the heroes lay down to rest.

"My plan," said Jason next morning when the heroes consulted together, "is to get the golden fleece without fighting, if possible. I shall ask King Aeetes for it, and from his own mouth we shall learn what course we must take. Now remain quietly here on the ship, my noble comrades, while I with two of your number will go to the palace."

King Aeetes received the Argonauts graciously. According to custom, he asked no questions until they were sitting down to food. But he no sooner learned who they

"I hold no grudge against brave men," he said. "But you must prove your courage. In the field of Ares I have two bulls whose feet are of bronze and whose breath is fire. You must yoke them and plow that field. Instead of grain, you must sow dragon's teeth. From them a crop of warriors will spring up. These you must slay before nightfall. All this I have done myself. If you cannot do it, I will not give up the fleece, for it is but just that the more valiant man shall have it."

Jason sat speechless and confused. How could he promise to perform such a hopeless task? At last he said:

"The labor which you ask is heavy. But I will undertake it—even though I perish in the attempt. There are worse things than death."

With this the Argonauts rose from the table and went back to their ship.

When the rest of the comrades heard what a fearful task Aeetes had set Jason, many offered to undertake the trial in his stead. But he refused them all.

"My destiny has brought me here," he said, "and come what may, I will obey it."

But now there came to them one of the king's grandsons, Argus by name, whom

Jason had by chance once rescued from a wrecked ship.

"Jason," he said, "there is no hope of your performing the labor my grandfather has set you. Let me, therefore, seek the help of Medea. She is my mother's young sister, and is a maiden skilled in brewing magic potions. Hecate herself, whose priestess she is, has taught her. She alone can enable you to yoke the fiery bulls and plow the fields of Ares."

"We are indeed in a sad plight if our safety depends on a woman," Jason answered him sadly. "But go to her if you like. I will not hinder you."

IN HECATE'S TEMPLE

UNKNOWN to either Jason or Argus, Medea was herself thinking hard how she might help the hero. For she had seen Jason as he sat at her father's table and had been stirred by his beauty and manliness. Never before had she felt love for a man, but now her feelings strove against one another and were stronger than herself. Many thoughts flew through her mind. Reason said one thing, her heart another.

"If I do not help him, this noble stranger will surely perish," she said to herself. "But shall I, then, betray my father's kingdom and rescue an unknown foreigner that he may go home and become another woman's husband? Ah, but he will not do that. Before I help him he will give me his promise to marry me. He will never deceive me or forget what I have done for him."

As she sat thus thinking, her sister came to her. "Medea," she said, "my son Argus, whose life you know Jason saved, has sent me to beg your help. Give the stranger some device, I pray, whereby he can overcome the bulls."

Medea's heart laughed when she heard her sister speak, but she hid her joy.

"I will do it," she said, "only for your son Argus' sake. Let him inform Jason that early in the morning I will go to Hecate's temple and there give him the magic with which he can survive the trial with the bulls."

So Jason came to Medea in the temple of Hecate. Never had he looked so handsome. When Medea's eyes rested on the stranger from Greece, she could not take them away. And when Jason took her hand, her heart fluttered so that she was speechless. For a long time they stood silent. Then Jason said:

"Lady, I come to beg you for the charm you promised. Ask in return what you will. And know that if you enable me and my companions to go home with the golden fleece, your glory will be undying. All Greece will praise you forever."

Medea did not answer—the tumult in her breast would not let her speak. She only placed a small box in Jason's hands. He stood holding the box tightly and gazing into her eyes, as much confused as she.

At last Medea spoke. "This is what you must do," she said, and told him what mystic rites he must perform and how to use the charm she had given him.

"Salve your body with this ointment," she said, "and also your weapons, that they be not consumed by fire. And when the warriors spring from the dragon's teeth, throw a great stone in their midst. That will cause them to turn one on another. And when all of them are dead, you can take the golden fleece and depart."

Tears gushed from Medea's eyes and rolled down her beautiful face as she said the last words and added, "Do not forget the name of Medea when you come home rejoicing, for she will be thinking of you."

"Never will I forget you, noble princess," Jason said passionately, "neither by night nor by day. But if you will come with me, all the men and women of Greece will adore you, for only because of you will their sons and husbands and brothers have returned home safe. And then nothing but death should stand between us."

Medea could have listened to his words without end, but the time had come to part. So, while Jason returned to his companions, she went back to the palace to struggle with her thoughts of loyalty and home and love.

THE FIERY BULLS

IT WAS scarcely dawn the next day when the townspeople assembled in the sacred field of Ares. They took their stand on the upper slopes. And in their midst King Aeetes sat clad in purple, his ivory sceptre in his hand. All eyes were on Jason, who stood upon the field examining the heavy yoke and plow.

Suddenly there was the sound of snorting and bellowing. Into the field rushed the brazen-footed bulls, wreathed in smoke and blowing fire from their mouths and nostrils. At the touch of their hot breath, the grass blazed up and roared as a furnace roars when it is stoked. Yet Jason went toward them. The creatures saw him and swung their awful heads from side to side. They bellowed and pawed the ground with their heavy cloven hoofs.

Rigid and breathless, the Argonauts watched from the slope as Jason boldly approached. Their hearts all but stood still when they saw Jason force first one bull, then the other, to its knees and harness the beasts to the yoke. And when the plow bit into the earth and turned up a black furrow, they broke into loud cheers, while all the Colchians stood amazed.

Jason plowed, and as he walked up the field and down, he kept taking from his helmet the dragon's teeth which had been given him and sowing them in the furrows. In the afternoon the four-acre field was done. Then Jason unyoked the bulls, and at his cry they fled in terror to their underground stable. When he turned, the crop of armed men was springing from the earth.

And now fear again took hold of the Argonauts, for they saw all the warriors prepare to hurl their spears at the hero. Even Medea felt a wave of panic surge over her as she beheld one solitary youth against so many men. Softly she chanted a spell to help him. But there was no need. Jason took up a great round stone and tossed it in the midst of the warriors, and immediately they turned on one another. To the last man they perished in that bloody war.

Then the Argonauts cheered so that the hills rang with the sound. Rushing down into the field, they hugged Jason in eager embraces. Even the Colchians shouted. But King Aeetes returned to the palace without a word. Anger gnawed at his heart. He knew that Jason could never have performed the labor without Medea's help, and he brooded into the night on vengeance and how he might outwit the clever Argonaut.

45

THE GOLDEN FLEECE

MEDEA passed the night in agony. She feared her father, but she also feared what might befall her if she fled with Jason. At last she made her decision. The palace doors opened at her magic spells, and she hurried to the shore where the Argonauts kept a great fire burning. At her call Jason leaped ashore.

"My father is planning fearful vengeance," Medea said. "Save yourselves and me from his wrath. I will get you the golden fleece. Only swear to me, swear that you will treat me honorably when I am a stranger in your native land."

"The gods be my witness that I shall make you my wife!" Jason promised.

"Then let us go at once and take the fleece," Medea said.

Quickly the ship carried them to the sacred grove, and together Jason and Medea approached the sacred oak. The dragon stretched his long neck toward them. He hissed fiercely. But Medea's charms lulled the creature to sleep, and for the first time the sleepless eyes closed. Then Jason snatched the golden fleece from the limb, and the two ran toward the ship.

With what wonder the Argonauts viewed the marvelous prize they had come so far to seek! But Jason, eager to depart, would not take time to let each man touch it.

"My noble comrades," he said, "let us be on our way, for we shall surely be pursued. And as for Medea here, know all of you that she who has helped us accomplish what we undertook shall be my lawful wife. I look to you to help me protect her, for she has rescued Greece."

So the Argonauts seated themselves hastily at the oars, and the vessel glided down the river and out upon the waves of the sea.

HOMEWARD BOUND

AS JASON fully expected, they had not long been out to sea before they saw Aeetes' fleet. The *Argo* had a good lead, but the Colchian ships were lighter and gained on it. And when Jason arrived at the

46

mouth of the Ister River, which empties into the Ionian Sea, the enemy ships were already lying in wait for him, scattered among the islands.

Jason was dismayed. "There are too many of the Colchians for us," he said. "Let us land and hold parley with them."

Now the leader of the Colchians was Acetes' son Apsyrtus, and King Aeetes had instructed him not to return without his sister Medea. So, as they parleyed, it was agreed that the Argonauts should carry off the golden fleece, but that Medea should be left in the temple of Artemis on another island. A king of those regions who was renowned for justice was to decide her fate. He should declare whether she should be returned to her father or go with Jason.

Medea nearly went out of her mind when she heard what Jason had agreed to.

"Jason," she cried, "have you forgotten your solemn vow to me? It is because of what I did for you that I am here! You know well that if I am taken home to my father I am lost. Oh, do not abandon me!"

She said this with such passion that Jason could not meet her eyes. So he took refuge in a lie.

"The agreement is just a ruse," he said. "We are trying to gain time and delay the battle. Our plan is to kill Apsyrtus, your brother. When the Colchians are without a leader, we can vanquish them."

Medea looked deep into false Jason's eyes, "If this is indeed your plan," she said, "I will go forward in crime. I will deliver my brother into your hands."

So she let Apsyrtus believe she had been carried away against her will. If he would come at night to the temple of Artemis, she would devise a way for him to get the golden fleece. Apsyrtus fell into the trap. And when that night he came to the temple and was alone with Medea, Jason rushed in and slew him with his sword. At a signal from Medea, the Argonauts fell on Apsyrtus' companions. They killed every one on his ship, and set off for Greece.

But when he arrived in Iolcus, Jason did not, after all, get the throne for the sake of which he had gone in search of the golden fleece. Medea did, indeed, contrive the death of Pelias. But in the end his son forced Jason to flee to Corinth. And it was here that the story of Jason and Medea had its terrible end.

WHEN THE VEIL WAS LIFTED

FOR ten years Medea and Jason lived together, man and wife. And to Medea they seemed like so many months for the love that she bore Jason. Exile though she was, her two loved sons and her husband, for whose sake she had left home and parents and committed every crime, made up to her for all. And then one day the veil was lifted from her eyes and she saw Jason as he was—a shallow, self-seeking man, treacherous and heartless.

In the ten years of Medea's love, Jason had grown tired of his Colchian wife. He had fallen in love with the young daughter of Creon, King of Corinth. Even more, he was eager to be in the family of such a king. So he wooed fair Glauce, but said nothing about it to Medea. Only when the wedding day was set, did Jason tell his wife of his plans and demand divorce.

In that hour all Medea's love turned to fierce hate. She yearned for one thing only— to strike back at Jason in some terrible way.

Now Medea, who had the reputation of being a witch, was unwise enough to speak her thoughts quite openly. So Creon, fearing that she would work some evil against Glauce, banished Medea and her young sons beyond the borders of the land. Then Medea denied that she had any evil designs. She implored Creon to let her remain in Corinth, and when he would not, she pleaded for just a single day. And this the King unwillingly granted her.

"It will be enough," Medea thought. "In this one day I will find some means to get revenge. Bitter and sad will I make their marriage for them!"

She was weighing in her mind one means and another when Jason came to her.

"Now I see," he said, "what a pest is a harsh temper. If you had patiently endured the will of your superiors, you might have remained in this land and house. But now for your idle words you are banished. You call me the basest of men. Yet I have come to see to it that you and your sons shall not be destitute when you are cast out. Though you hate me, I have no hard thoughts of you."

"You craven villain," Medea replied, "do you come to me? It is not proof of courage to face your friends after injuring them, but loss of shame. Yet you have done well to come, for it will ease my soul to show you what you are."

And Medea poured out all she had done for him from the beginning, reminded him of his vows, pointed out that she could not go home again and had no other place to go. To serve Jason she had made enemies of people she need never have wronged.

"I am without a single friend," she said. "A fine reproach it is to you in your bridal hour that your children and the wife who saved your life are beggars and vagabonds."

Jason did not even flush. "For saving my life you received more than ever you gave," he answered coolly. "Do you not live in Greece instead of in a barbarian land? Have you not become famous because of your deed? It is not because I am smitten with desire for a new bride that I have made this marriage. It is that you and your sons may live in comfort through this alliance."

"I do not want such wealth as would ever sting my heart!" Medea cried. Nor would she take anything from Jason. "A villain's gifts can bring no blessing," she said, and drove him from her door.

Afterwards she regretted it and sent for Jason again—for he was necessary to her plans. She hid her bitter hate. She pretended she did not care at all about the marriage.

"Plead with your young bride to let the children stay and that I alone be exiled," she begged Jason. "And I myself will help you persuade her. I will send her by the children's hand a wedding gift of surpassing beauty—a robe of finest tissue and a chaplet of chased gold. To save my children from exile, I will part with these great treasures. For gifts tempt even the gods and hold greater sway over the minds of men than countless words."

So the robe and the chaplet came into the bride's hands, and with a happy smile she put them on. But soon she turned pale, reeled backwards, and sank upon a seat. Foam came from her mouth, her eyeballs rolled. Suddenly she shrieked and started from her seat. The robe and the chaplet of gold, which Medea had soaked in fiercest poison, sent forth flames. All on fire, the bride fell to the floor. By the time her father came running, she was dead. Creon threw himself upon her lamenting, and the fearful poison entered into his flesh, too. Father and daughter lay dead together.

Medea rejoiced when she heard the news from the lips of the messenger who brought her children back. But she had not done with Jason yet.

And now he came, all shattered by the blow, to save his sons. For he feared that Creon's kin might take revenge on them, as well as on Medea.

He came too late. Already the boys were dead. Medea herself had murdered the sons she loved, to punish Jason fully.

In vain he hammered on the door—Medea would not let him see nor touch his murdered boys.

"O my children, how vile a mother you have found!" he cried.

And through the fast-shut door he heard Medea answer: "Not my hand, but your foul treatment of me slew them."

"Give up to me these dead to bury and lament!" Jason pleaded.

"No! I will bury them myself."

There was silence. Then Jason heard a rushing in the air overhead. He looked up. In a chariot drawn by fiery dragons, Medea was fleeing Corinth.

DAEDALUS

In the days when King Minos ruled Crete and his mighty navy ranged the seas, there lived in Athens a man by the name of Daedalus. And his name was known as far and wide as that of Minos. For Daedalus was the greatest architect and sculptor of his time. There was nothing his ingenious mind could not design or his skillful hands execute. And his statues were so real that people said they lived. It seemed that at any moment they might move a hand or take a step or open their lips and speak.

His young nephew, Talus, also had clever hands and a creative mind. So his mother placed him with her brother that the boy might learn his marvelous skills. But Talus had a genius of his own and even more imagination. Walking on the shore one day, he picked up the backbone of a fish. Idly he drew the strong, sharp spines forward and back across a piece of driftwood. They cut deep into the wood. He went home and notched a metal blade all along one edge—and he had a saw. Another time he fixed two iron rods together at the tip. He held one firmly upright against the earth and moved the other slowly around. It made a perfect circle—he had invented the compass.

Talus was a pupil to make any teacher excited and proud. But not Daedalus. Instead of being pleased, he was frightened and sorely jealous.

"Talus will soon surpass me!" he thought.

He could not bear the idea of a rival, and came to hate the boy. And one day, when they stood together on a height, Daedalus pushed Talus off to his death.

He had not planned the deed. It had been a sudden, crazy impulse. The next instant, horrified at what he had done, he rushed down to the boy. But it was too late. Talus was dead, and not all the wonderful skills of Daedalus could call him back. Clearly, if Daedalus wished to save his own life, he must flee. So he left Athens and wandered miserably from place to place, until at last he left Greece altogether and crossed the sea to Crete.

King Minos was delighted to have the Athenian in his realm. The King had something in mind that called for the genius of Daedalus. Minos possessed a fearful monster, with the head and shoulders of a bull and the legs and trunk of a man. The creature was called the Minotaur—that is, the Bull of Minos. The King wanted a suitable place to keep the Minotaur. The building must be such that neither the monster himself nor any victim sent in to be devoured by him could possibly escape from it.

So, at the King's command, Daedalus designed the Labyrinth. The building was a bewildering maze of passages. They turned back upon themselves, crisscrossed, and went round and round without leading anywhere. Once inside the Labyrinth, it was all but impossible to find the way out again. Even Daedalus himself was once nearly lost.

King Minos was delighted with Daedalus' work and held him in highest favor. Yet Daedalus was less than pleased, for he felt himself to be no better than a prisoner in Crete. The King was so afraid Daedalus would reveal the secret of the Labyrinth that he would not let him leave the island. And for that very reason Daedalus yearned to go. With what envy he watched the birds winging their way through the sky!

One day, as his eyes followed the graceful sea birds cleaving the ocean of air, an idea came to him.

"King Minos may shut my way out by land and by sea," he thought, "but he does not control the air."

And he began to study the flight of birds and to observe how their wings are fashioned. He watched the little song birds fold and unfold their wings, watched how they rose from the ground, flew down from the trees, and went to and fro. He also watched the herons slowly flapping their great wings. He watched the eagles soar and swoop. He saw, too, how their feathers overlapped one another—where they were large and where they were small.

When he thought he understood the secrets of flight, Daedalus went to a nesting place he knew of and gathered feathers of various sizes. And in a chamber close to the roof he began to build wings. First he laid down a row of the tiniest feathers, then a row of larger ones overlapping them, and yet larger ones beyond these. He fastened the feathers together in the middle with thread

and at the bottom with wax. And when he had built on enough rows, he bent them around into a gentle curve to look like real birds' wings.

His young son Icarus stood by and watched his father work. Laughing, the boy caught the feathers when they blew away in the wind. He pressed his thumb into the yellow wax to soften it for his father, hindering more than he helped.

When Daedalus had finished the pair of wings, he put them on. He raised himself in the air and hovered there. He moved the wings just as he had seen birds do, and lo! he could fly. Icarus clapped his hands together in delight.

"Make me a pair of wings, too, father!" he cried.

Then Daedalus made a second pair of wings and prepared his son to fly.

"Now I warn you, Icarus," Daedalus said, "not to be reckless. Be wise, not bold. Take a course midway between heaven and earth. For if you fly too high, the sun will scorch your feathers. And if you fly too low, the sea will wet them. Take me for your guide. Follow me and you will be safe."

All the time he was speaking, Daedalus was fastening the wings to his son's shoulders. His hands trembled as he thought of the great adventure before them. At the same time, he was worried about the boy. He did not know whether he could quite trust Icarus to obey. As he adjusted his own wings and kissed the excited child, tears ran down Daedalus' face.

"Remember," he repeated for the last time. "Heed my words and stay close to me!"

Then he rose on his wings and flew from the housetop. Icarus followed.

Daedalus kept a watchful eye on the boy, even as a mother bird does when she has brought a fledgling out of its nest in the tree-tops and launched it in the air. It was early morning. Few people were about. But here and there a plowman in the field or a fisherman tending his nets caught sight of them.

"They must be gods!" the simple toilers cried, and they bent their bodies in reverent worship.

Father and son flew far out over the sea. Daedalus was no longer worried about Icarus, who managed his wings as easily as a bird. Already the islands of Delos and Paros were behind them. Calymne, rich in honey, was on their right hand. But now Icarus began to yield to the full delight of his new-found powers. He wanted to soar and swoop. How thrilling it was to rise to a height, close his wings, and speed down, down, like a thunderbolt, then turn and rise again!

Time after time Icarus tried it, each time daring greater heights. Then, forgetting his father's warning, he soared higher still, far up into the cloudless sky.

"Not even the eagle soars as high as this!" the boy thought. "I am like the gods that keep the wide heaven."

As the words crossed his mind, he felt a warm stream flow over his shoulders. He

had come too close to the blazing sun, and the sweet-smelling wax that bound the feathers was melting. With a shock of terror he felt himself hurtling downward. His wings, broken in a thousand parts, were hurtling downward, too. In vain Icarus moved his arms up and down—he could get no hold on the air.

"Father!" he shrieked. "Father! Help! I am falling."

Even as he cried, the deep blue water of the sea—that ever since has been called Icarian—closed over him.

"Icarus! Icarus! Where are you?" Daedalus cried, turning in every direction and searching the air behind, above, and all around. Then his eyes fell on the sea. Tufts of feathers were floating on the crest of the waves.

Too well he understood their meaning. Folding his great wings, he came to earth on the nearest island and fixed his streaming eyes upon the sea. He beat his breast. Wildly he clutched his hair.

"O Icarus, my son!" he wailed. "Even so fell Talus whom my envy slew! The gods have avenged him." He ripped off his glorious wings and stamped upon them. "Cursed be the skill that wrought my son's destruction!" he cried.

Days afterwards, the body of Icarus washed to the shore. There, on the lonely island which bears the boy's name, Daedalus buried his only son.

THESEUS AND THE MINOTAUR
SANDALS AND A SWORD

IN THE palace of old King Pittheus of Troezen a grandson was growing up—brave, strong, and handsome. And people said of him: "What wonder that Theseus is so fair and noble? Is not the great god Poseidon his father?"

The young Theseus was pleased enough with being a god's son, the more especially as his cousin Heracles was one. For Theseus idolized the hero whose praises sounded in every court. Often the boy said to himself, "I will be like Heracles and slay wild beasts and giants and evil men." So it was a shock to him to learn that he was no demigod but the son of a mortal—King Aegeus of Athens.

The secret was revealed to him in a curious way. For several years past on his birthday, his mother, the Princess Aethra, had taken him to a great black stone standing by the sea.

"My son," she had always said, "see if you can push this stone aside."

Try as he would, he had never been able to do it. But on his eighteenth birthday he had scarcely exerted his strength when the mighty rock yielded, disclosing a hollow beneath, and in the hollow lay a gold-hilted sword and a pair of embroidered sandals.

"This sword and these sandals were your father's," Theseus' mother said. "Take them up, for now they are yours."

Then she told him about her secret marriage to King Aegeus and how on parting from her he had said: "When my son—if you bear a son—is strong enough to move this stone, give him my sword and my sandals and let him come to Athens and make himself known to me."

Theseus at once put on the sandals and strapped the great gold-hilted sword by his side. He was all on fire to go to Athens.

"I will provide you with a vessel and oarsmen," his grandfather King Pittheus said. "For the roads are beset with robbers."

"Indeed, indeed, grandfather, I will go by land," Theseus protested. "For how can I come to my father with his sword unstained? Greece rings with the fame of Heracles my cousin, and shall I avoid robbers rather than slay them?"

Theseus pleaded so hard that in the end King Pittheus, great as were his fears, gave in and said, "Do according to your spirit."

So Theseus set out on foot and alone.

ON THE WAY TO ATHENS

ow as the young traveler strode lightly along, his mind busy with thoughts of Athens and high deeds, the first of the evildoers who beset the way rushed out at him from the woods. A black bearskin cloaked his bulky body and an iron club was in his hand. He stood squarely in the path, brandishing his weapon and shouting fearful threats.

Theseus did not draw back. "To slay villains like you, have I come this way!" he cried and flung himself boldly on the attacker.

Not in vain had the prince labored to perfect himself in wrestling and boxing. He soon left the savage dead upon the ground. But the iron club he took away and ever after carried with him. Did not Heracles his cousin also bear a club?

Many a time on that journey Theseus was glad of the powerful weapon. For the way to Athens, as his grandfather had warned, was infested with robbers. Three more scoundrels he slew before he reached the river Cephisus not far from Athens. And had not chance put him on his guard, before crossing that river, he might have lost his life. For now there came toward him a villain of another sort, a fellow richly clad and smiling and pleasant of speech.

"Noble traveler," he said to Theseus, "you must come with me and eat and drink of the best my house affords, for it is my custom to show hospitality to all who pass this way."

"I am in haste," Theseus answered, thanking him courteously.

But the other seized hold of Theseus' hands and would not let him go. Theseus did not like to offend one who seemed so hospitable. So against his will he followed the stranger to his house.

Now while they sat at table, his host was called from the chamber, and the slave who poured the wine, whispered to Theseus:

"Young man, flee this house while yet you may! My master is a monster of evil. He will bid you sleep in his famed iron bed which fits all men. Once you are asleep, he will bind you to it. If you are too long for his bed, he will cut off your legs. If you are too short, he will stretch you to fit. Therefore is he called Procrustes, the Stretcher."

Theseus said no word, but grasped his club, which he had laid down by him. And before he left that house, he had fitted Procrustes to his own bed.

THESEUS MEETS HIS FATHER

News of the hero's exploits traveled fast. Long before Theseus arrived, Aegeus knew that a brave youth from Troezen was on his way to Athens. But the King had no thought that this was his son and anxiously awaited his arrival. For Athens was in turmoil, and the childless King was afraid.

"The people might set him on the throne in my place," he thought.

Now Aegeus' wife was none other than Medea, that same Medea who had taken such fearful revenge on Jason. In her chariot drawn by dragons she had escaped through the air to Athens. There she had gained great influence over the old King and had then got him to marry her. She knew who Theseus was. She, too, feared his coming. But it was for a different reason. "With a hero son by his side, the king will no longer hearken to me as of old," she thought.

And she said to Aegeus: "Let us poison Theseus at the first opportunity. For I have learned by my magic arts that he comes to destroy you."

So when with welcoming cries the Athenians brought the hero to the palace, Aegeus received him graciously, hiding for the moment his evil intentions. Theseus, for his part, was all eagerness. He could hardly wait

to make himself known to his father. But the Prince had set his heart on having Aegeus recognize him of his own accord. So he gave no reason for his coming and accepted the King's hospitality merely as any hero might do.

Morning came. Theseus took his place beside Aegeus at the meal that had been set forth. A goblet of wine stood at the youth's place, and Aegeus watched eagerly to see Theseus drain it, for Medea had mixed a deadly poison for him. But Theseus did not even notice the wine. His happy eyes were turned on his father and he waited, a smile on his parted lips, hoping to be recognized. When Aegeus made no sign, the hero quietly laid his sword on the table.

A look of horror spread over Aegeus' face and a loud cry escaped him as he beheld the golden hilt. He reached across the table and dashed the fatal goblet to the floor. Then, weeping, he took his son in his arms and hugged him and passed his hands over the stalwart body and felt the knotting muscles and kissed the fair beardless cheeks of his hero son. Nor could Theseus look enough upon his father.

But Medea knew well that her hour had come, knew well that her witching rule in Athens was over. So once again she summoned her swift-flying dragons. And once more they bore her away—none knew where.

THE MINOTAUR

Not long after Aegeus had acknowledged Theseus as his son and heir, Athens was thrown into mourning. Heralds had arrived from Crete to demand for the third time the terrible human tribute which every nine years had to be paid to King Minos.

Years before, Androgeos, the son of Minos, had gone to Athens to take part in the games. He had shown great prowess, overcoming all the Greeks. Provoked by this, Aegeus had treacherously caused Androgeos to be slain, whereupon King Minos made war on him. The King of Crete raised a great fleet and pressed Aegeus so hard that he was

glad to make peace at any price. And the price was terrible—a tribute of seven youths and seven maidens to be sent to Crete and thrown to the Minotaur, the monster half-man, half-bull that lived in the Labyrinth.

Theseus saw that the Athenians were deeply angry with his father, who had brought this grief upon them. At once he offered to go to Minos.

"No, no, my son!" Aegeus pleaded. "The victims will be chosen by lot. Wait and see if you are selected. I have but newly found you!"

But Theseus was like a rock. "I will be one of the fourteen," he said, "whether I am chosen or not."

So Aegeus had to yield. Weeping, and with all Athens following, he went with the victims to the dismal ship.

"O my father, do not weep so," Theseus told him. "All is as the gods will. It may indeed be my fate to slay the Minotaur, and we who sail today in sorrow may yet return in joy. If so, you will know the good news from afar. For I promise you, if the Minotaur be slain, the ship that brings us home will not wear these deadly black sails but victorious white ones."

After this the vessel took to the sea, the land slipped away, and the youths and maidens turned their faces toward Crete.

At Cnossos, the capital of Crete, crowds gathered to see the Athenians whom the Minotaur would soon devour. With many a taunt the captives were paraded in front of the palace. Everyone ran out to see the victims, and with them Ariadne, King Minos' lovely daughter. She stood with a throng of her maidens and looked on as did the rest. But her gentle eyes fixed themselves on one alone—on princely Theseus, who, head high and eyes proudly flashing, marched looking neither to the right nor to the left. A surge of sudden love swept over the princess. And as the taunts rose all around her, she promised herself: "He shall not die!"

As soon as night fell, Ariadne stole out of the palace and went secretly to the captives.

"Fair youth," she whispered to Theseus, "I who for my brother's sake should be your enemy am not. Therefore, I have brought you this." And she took from the folds of her dress a glistening sword and put it in Theseus' hand.

He grasped it joyfully and strapped it beneath his garments.

"Now let the Minotaur roar as loud as he will—he will roar in vain!" Theseus said. "Thanks, gracious Princess. May I live to serve you!"

Ariadne then confessed her love, and Theseus, who found it easy enough to give his in return, promised ardently to make her his wife.

"Indeed I would have it so," Ariadne said. "But there is one thing more," she added. "Without it the sword would be useless, for you would never be able to find your way out of the Labyrinth, which the Athenian Daedalus built. The Minotaur's house is a maze. The passages turn and turn and lead into one another and end nowhere. None who enters may come forth again. Take, therefore, this ball of thread. Tie one end to the inside of the door and unwind the ball as you go. Then, winding it again, you will be able to retrace your steps."

So it was that the hero met the Minotaur in the gloomy depths of the Labyrinth and was not afraid. He came upon the monster sleeping and leaped on him and battled furiously with him. And when the creature lay dead at his feet, Theseus picked up the ball of thread and wound it back to the entrance.

What joy there was when Theseus' glad voice resounded through the passages and his companions saw their leader emerge! What embracing, what happy talk of home! With stealthy steps they made their way to their vessel, where Ariadne stood anxiously waiting for them. Deftly they hoisted sail, dipped their oars, and left the harbor so noiselessly that the Cretans never awoke to realize their loss.

Meantime at Athens King Aegeus daily mounted the cliffs by the sea and sorrowfully strained his old eyes in the direction of Crete. At last he saw the ship approaching—and his heart died within him. Black sails drank the wind. In the joy of homecoming, Theseus had forgotten to change the dismal sails of mourning.

"My son is dead!" the unhappy King cried out. "Why, then, do I live?"

Grief overpowered him and he cast himself headlong into the sea, which ever after has borne his name.

OEDIPUS

A KING IS SLAIN

KING Laius ruled Thebes of the Seven Gates, and he was an unhappy man. For an oracle had warned him that he would be slain by his own son.

Laius prayed that he might have no children. But the gods were deaf to his prayers, and a son was born to him and Queen Jocasta.

"Better that our son should die than live to murder his father," they told each other with great anguish.

Then Laius pierced the baby's ankles, tied them together with a thong, and gave the child over to a shepherd, telling him to abandon the baby in the mountains of Cythaeron.

The shepherd took the newborn child and went his way. But pity would not let him carry out the King's command. Secretly he took the baby to a brother shepherd who on those same mountains pastured the flocks of King Polybus of Corinth. And this man in turn gave the baby over to King Polybus himself, who, being childless, brought the boy up as his own son. And the child was given the name Oedipus—*Swollen-foot*—because the cruel thong had done its work.

Young Oedipus grew to splendid strength and manhood in the palace of the King. He had no thought but that Polybus was his father and Queen Merope his mother. But one day at a banquet where wine flowed freely, a young Corinthian who was envious of the prince taunted him, saying:

"You who think yourself so nobly born are not the true son of King Polybus!"

Oedipus made no reply. He suffered out the day in silence. But next morning he went to the King and Queen and demanded to know the truth. They tried most lovingly to reassure him. But doubt had struck deep into Oedipus' soul and he could not rest.

"I will go to the oracle at Delphi," he decided, "and ask Phoebus Apollo whether I am truly the son of Polybus or not." And, saying no word of his plan to anyone, he set out.

To his dismay, the oracle, instead of replying to his question, answered him with the fearful prophecy: "You will slay your father and marry your mother."

"No, that I will never do!" Oedipus promised himself. "Rather will I never set eyes on my parents again!" And he turned his face from home, taking the road to Boeotia.

Now he had not gone far from Delphi when he came to a place where three roads met. Coming toward him was a chariot in which there were five persons. One was a tall man with graying hair, one a herald, one was the charioteer, and two were servants.

"Out of the way, fellow!" the charioteer shouted, crowding Oedipus from the narrow way. The Prince, who had a hot temper and was not used to getting out of the way for anybody, struck out at the insolent charioteer. At this the old man brought his goad with its two teeth down on Oedipus' head.

Then Oedipus turned mad with rage. Raising the staff he carried, he struck back at the old man with all his strength, and toppled him over backwards out of the chariot. In the fight that followed, the Prince was one against three—for one of the attendants fled without striking a blow—yet when he left, all three were dead upon the ground beside their master.

Oedipus never dreamed as he went his way that already the first part of the oracle had been fulfilled. For the old man in the chariot was King Laius of Thebes, who had been journeying to Delphi to consult Apollo. Nor did Laius, dying instantly as he fell, have time to learn that the oracle he had tried so hard to escape had been fulfilled.

THE RIDDLE OF THE SPHINX

NOT LONG after this, another sorrow befell Thebes. A winged monster with a woman's head and a lion's body began to prey on all who traveled to and from the city past the cliff on which she crouched.

The Sphinx had learned a difficult riddle and was amusing herself by demanding the answer from every passer-by. Whoever could not give the right answer—and none as yet had been able to do it—was torn to pieces and devoured.

Now when King Laius had so unaccountably been slain, Queen Jocasta's brother, Creon, had taken over the rule of Thebes. But after Creon's own son fell victim to the Sphinx, the heartbroken father lost all desire to rule. He caused a proclamation to be made that whoever freed the city from the monster should become king and have Queen Jocasta as his wife.

The herald was just making this announcement when Oedipus arrived in Thebes. The Prince had traveled by a different road and had not met the Sphinx.

But now he said to himself, "What is life worth with so terrible an oracle hanging over me!" And he went out to seek the monster.

From afar off he saw her upon the cliff. Undaunted, he drew near and called out:

"Ask me your riddle, and I will answer you as best I can.

The Sphinx promptly spoke her riddle, which she believed impossible to guess: "What animal is it that goes in the morning on four feet, at noon on two, and in the evening on three?"

"It is man!" Oedipus replied at once. "For in the morning of his life he crawls on both hands and feet. At noon, when he is strong, he walks on two. And in the evening of life, when he is weak and needs support, he leans on a staff, which is a third foot for him."

The Sphinx gave a horrid shriek, for Oedipus had given the right answer. Fuming with rage, she leaped from the cliff and was dashed to pieces on the ground.

So Oedipus became king of Thebes and married Queen Jocasta, thereby fulfilling the second half of the oracle—that he would marry his own mother.

THE SEER TIRESIAS

YEARS passed. Children were born to Oedipus, two sons and two daughters. He was loved and honored by all, was rich, mighty, renowned. Thebes was prosperous as never before. And no one thought any more about old King Laius, the mystery of whose death had never been solved.

But now again trouble fell on the city—a pestilence began to rage. Young and old fell before the angry waves of death. A blight was on the fruitful blossoms. In the pastures the flocks and herds perished and were barren. The stricken city reeked with incense and rang with prayers and cries of woe.

Then the priests said to Oedipus, "It is clear that this plague is a punishment for some grave sin. Send to Delphi to ask the god by what word or deed the city can be delivered."

So Oedipus sent his brother-in-law Creon. And Creon came back with Apollo's answer: "An evil is being harbored in this land; the murderers of Laius must be found and vengeance done."

"I will leave nothing untried," Oedipus declared, "to find him whose hand shed that blood." And he began to question into what happened long ago.

"Why did you not search at the time and find out the murderers?" he asked Creon.

"The riddling Sphinx made us forget everything else," Creon answered. "We had to think of what lay at our doors."

"I will start afresh," Oedipus said. And he addressed the people:

"Justly said," Oedipus answered. "But no man on earth can force the gods to do what they will not."

"Then send for Tiresias, the blind seer."

"At the suggestion of Creon I have already twice sent a man to bring him," Oedipus answered. "This long while I marvel why he is not here."

He had hardly said this when a boy led in the blind Tiresias. Oedipus at once told him what answer Creon had brought from the god.

"Use all means in your power to solve the

"Whosoever of you knows by whom Laius was slain, I bid him declare all to me, and not be afraid, for he shall only leave the land and nothing more shall be done to him. But if you keep silence or seek to shield a friend or yourself, hear what I shall do. I charge you that no one of this land give shelter or speak word to that murderer, whosoever he be, or let him take part in prayer or sacrifice. I pray solemnly that the slayer may wear out his life unblessed. And for myself, I pray that if with my knowledge he should become an inmate of my house, I may suffer the same things which even now I called down upon others."

"Phoebus himself should tell us who it was that did that murderous deed," one of the citizens of Thebes put in.

mystery," the King urged. "Rescue the city, rescue me, rescue us all. For we are in your hand."

"Let me go home," Tiresias answered. "It will be best for you if I go."

"For the love of the gods, turn not away if you have knowledge!" Oedipus cried.

But the blind seer would not reveal what he knew. "The future will come of itself," he said.

Then Oedipus grew angry. He made threats. Still the seer refused to speak. "Rage if you will," he said, "with the fiercest wrath your heart knows."

"I will speak all my thought," Oedipus said in a passion. "You seem to me to have helped in plotting that murder. If you had eyesight, I would have said you did that deed yourself."

Tiresias could bear no more.

"Say you so?" he cried. "Then abide by your own decree and from this day speak neither to these people nor to me! For *you* are the accursed defiler of this land. *You* are the slayer of the man whose slayer you seek.

And you have been living in guilty union with your nearest kin."

Oedipus was stunned. He could interpret the accusation in just one way: "It is clear that you, maimed in wit and eye, are in Creon's pay and are trying to force me, Oedipus who silenced the Sphinx and saved the city, from my throne!"

"King though you are," the blind man answered, "the right of reply is the same for both of us. And I tell you—since you have taunted me with blindness—that though you have sight, you do not see your misery, nor where you live, nor with whom. All Cithaeron shall soon ring with your shriek when you have learned the meaning of your marriage. Therefore heap your scorn on Creon and on me as much as you please. No one among men shall ever be crushed more miserably than you. You who now have sight shall be a blind man. You who now are rich shall be a beggar and shall make your way to a strange land, feeling the ground before you with your staff."

And with those bitter words, Tiresias departed, led out by the boy.

THE MYSTERY UNFOLDS

Now Creon came hurrying to Oedipus. He had heard the accusation against himself and bitterly denied scheming for the throne. But Oedipus refused to believe him. He threatened Creon with banishment or death. If Queen Jocasta had not then come out to stop the quarrel and the people themselves had not interfered, Oedipus would surely have carried out this threat.

"Tell me how the quarrel began," Jocasta said when her brother had gone.

"He says that I stand guilty of the blood of Laius," Oedipus answered, "and accuses me through Tiresias."

"Then hear this, and be comforted," Jocasta said, "for you will see how little these seers know. An oracle came to Laius once that he should die by the hand of his son. But when a son was born to him, Laius pinned its ankles together and had it thrown on a track-

less mountain. And later he was slain by robbers at a place where three roads meet. So, you see, the oracle did not come to pass."

At Jocasta's words, Oedipus' heart seemed to stop beating.

"Laius slain where three roads meet?" he asked. "Where? When?"

"The land is called Phocis," Jocasta replied. "The branching roads lead to the same spot from Delphi and from Daulia. The news of

the murder was made known shortly before you took over the rule of this land."

"O Zeus," Oedipus cried, "what have you decreed for me?"

"Why does this thing weigh so on your soul?" Jocasta asked anxiously.

"Do not ask me yet," the King answered. "But tell me how tall Laius was, and how old he was."

"He was tall. The silver was just lightly strewn among his hair, and his form was not greatly unlike yours."

"Tell me one thing more. Was he with many armed followers, like a chieftain?"

"They were five in all."

"And who brought you the tidings?"

"A servant—the sole survivor who came home."

"Let him be sent for," Oedipus said.

"He shall come," Jocasta answered. "But I, too, have a right to learn what lies heavy on your heart, my king."

Then Oedipus told her how he had gone to Delphi to learn who his father was; how he had received the oracle that he would slay his father and marry his mother; how he had met five men in a chariot and had slain all but one who fled.

"And if the old man was indeed Laius," Oedipus said, "who is now more wretched than the man before you? What mortal could be more hated by heaven? No citizen may receive me in his house or speak to me or give me shelter. And this curse was laid on me by no one but myself. I have married the wife of the man I slew. Am I not vile? I must be banished. Nor can I go home to my own land and parents unless I would marry my mother, Merope, and slay my father, Polybus."

Oedipus still did not see the truth. He did not guess that he was Laius' son. He even clung to the hope that perhaps he was not the slayer of the king.

"The man who fled spoke of Laius as slain by robbers," he said. "If when he comes, he still speaks as before of several robbers, then I was not the slayer."

"Be assured," Jocasta said as they entered the palace, "that thus the tale was first told. He cannot say otherwise, for the whole city heard it, not I alone."

"ALL BROUGHT TO PASS — ALL TRUE!"

Now, meantime, a messenger from Corinth had arrived with news that Polybus was dead and that the people wished to make Oedipus their king.

When she heard the tidings, Jocasta said joyfully to her handmaiden:

"Away with all speed and tell this to your master. Now he will see how little trust is to be put in oracles! Polybus is the man whom Oedipus long feared and shunned lest he should slay him. And now this man has died a natural death."

Oedipus was, indeed, much relieved to hear that Polybus had died of sickness and old age.

"It is clear now," he said, "that oracles are worth nothing."

But still he doubted, still he feared to go home to Corinth because of Merope. For had not the oracle said that he should wed his own mother?

"Was it for fear of this that you were an exile from Corinth?" the messenger asked Oedipus. "Then know that you have no reason to fear. Polybus was nothing to you in blood. He was no more your father than I am. He received you as a gift from my hands long ago. It was I who saved you and freed you when your ankles were pinned together by a thong."

And then with horror Oedipus learned that this man had received him from another shepherd, one of the household of King Laius.

"Is that man still alive that I may see him?" the King asked.

"I think," a citizen said, "he is no other than the peasant whom you have already sent for. But our lady Jocasta might best tell you that."

The Queen stood with her hands over her face, for the terrible truth had come to her at last.

"Why ask of whom he spoke?" she stammered. "Waste not a thought on what he said! For the sake of the gods, if you have any care for your own life, search no further! My anguish is enough."

"Be of courage," Oedipus said to her, mistaking the reason of her anguish. "Though I be found to be the son of a peasant mother, you will not be proved base-born."

"Ill-fated me!" Jocasta wailed. "May you never come to know who you are! This only can I say to you and no other word henceforth for ever!" And she rushed wildly into the palace.

She had scarcely gone when the shepherd who had been sent for was brought in.

Oedipus turned to the messenger from Corinth. "I ask you first," the King said, "is this he whom you mean?"

"This is the man."

Then Oedipus questioned the shepherd. He denied having known the man from Corinth, and only by force was Oedipus able to make him speak. Step by step, the story unfolded, until at last Oedipus knew all.

"Oh, oh! All brought to pass—all true!" he moaned. "Light, may I now look my last on you—I who have been found accursed in birth, accursed in wedlock, accursed in the shedding of blood!" And he, too, rushed wildly into the palace.

The terrified citizens stood outside talking of the ills within when a man came out.

"Our royal lady Jocasta is dead!" he announced. "Dead by her own hand. We saw it not till Oedipus burst open the door of her chamber. Then we beheld her hanging by the neck on a twisted noose. When the King saw her, he uttered a deep cry of misery and loosed the halter whereby she hung. And when she lay on the ground, he tore the gold brooches from her garments, and lifted them, and smote his own eye-balls, crying, 'Long enough have you looked on those whom you ought never to have seen—henceforth you shall be dark!'"

"And what does he now?"

"He cries for someone to unbar the gates and lead him from the land."

So did the prophecy of Tiresias come to pass. A blind man, a beggar, feeling the ground before him with a staff, Oedipus went forth from Thebes.

BEOWULF

GRENDEL, HATER OF MEN

"COME, my henchmen," King Hrothgar said to his Danes, "let us build us a mead-hall, high and gabled, huger than any known to men. There we will revel and make good cheer. The sound of harp and song shall be heard, and I will distribute to young and old such gifts as God gave me, except the land and the lives of my men."

So skilled workmen came from many countries and fashioned a noble hall. Heorot it was called—the Hart—because of the antlers high on the gabled walls. Its fame spread far. "Happy are Hrothgar's thanes," folk said in distant lands.

But in his dark abode, the grim monster Grendel heard with envy and anger the din of revel in the hall. He heard the harps ring out, and the clear songs of the singers. At fall of night Grendel went forth. He found the lofty hall where, after the feast, the thanes had gone to sleep. He burst open the door. Savage and gluttonous, he seized thirty of the sleeping warriors and rushed back to his lair.

There was moaning and wailing in Heorot when at dawn the strength of Grendel was known, and the trail of blood was traced to the lake. The chief sat grieving for the loss of his men. But pause there was none—with the return of darkness, murder started anew. Night after gloomy night the terrible monster came to Heorot, till none dared sleep in the hall. Silent and empty stood that lordly building after set of sun. At dark it was a place of dread.

Thus for twelve years the terror went on. The lonely roamer preyed on the Danes, one against all. He ambushed young and old. The fiend would not make peace for gold, nor did altar offerings help. He lorded over Heorot. And tidings of the hater of men spread far in sorrowful songs.

A HERO COMES

IN SWEDEN, in the land of the Geats, stalwart young Beowulf heard of the murderous doings of Grendel. And he said to Hygelac, his uncle and lord:

"Our good friend Hrothgar is desperate for men. I will go over the water and seek that battle-king and slay the slaughtering monster that brings him sorrow."

"I pray you," Hygelac answered, "do not go. Let the Danes settle their feud with Grendel themselves. I have no faith in this far sea venture."

But Beowulf had a vessel fitted and furnished, and gathered about him the keenest of warriors. Fourteen chosen comrades followed him to the stout ship that lay waiting under a bluff. The billows were breaking, sea against sand, as they boarded the vessel. Snugly they stowed their trappings and battle gear. Then over the wind-whipped water the sea-wood sped like a bird with breast of foam. And already on the second day, the warriors could see the shining headlands of Denmark.

Now, as with clatter of armor they waded ashore and made their ship fast, a warrior who guarded the coast saw them.

"What men are you that have brought that tall ship to our land?" he asked. "Where do you come from?"

"We are of the Geat clan," Beowulf answered. "Hygelac's hearth-companions are we. We have heard of the murdering monster that comes on gloomy nights to show his rage. We would bring help to Hrothgar your lord."

"March, then, with your weapons; the way I will show you. I judge you are loyal," the guard said. "And I will bid my men watch your ship till the survivors return."

Joyful was Hrothgar, sitting on his high-seat in the timbered hall, when Beowulf's band was brought before him. Hope stirred again in the old King's breast. He had heard of Beowulf's prowess, had heard that he had the strength of thirty men in his grip.

"Hail, Hrothgar!" Beowulf said. "Hygelac's kinsman am I. Word of Grendel's deeds has reached the Geats, and I have come to destroy the murdering monster. One boon I ask of you, though—and do not refuse it, now I have come so far—that I alone with this hardy band may sweep Heorot clean of him. Grendel, I hear, has no respect for weapons. So I will bear neither sword nor shield, but with my grip alone shall face the fiend. We will fight for life, body against body. If he wins, he is sure to eat my Geatish band here in this gilded hall, as often before he has devoured your noblest warriors. Nor will you have to bury me, either; for he will carry me off, covered with blood."

"Beowulf, my friend," the old King replied, "it is hard for me to speak of what Grendel's hate has done in Heorot. My warriors grow few. In times past many of them boasted over the ale-cup that they would await Grendel's attack here in the mead-hall. When daylight came, the benches were drenched with blood, and I had so many heroes the less. . . But sit down to the banquet now, valiant Geat, and speak what words your heart shall bid."

So they drank, Danes and Geats together, and boasted of prowess, one and another. Then high-born Wealhtheow came forward, Hrothgar's Queen, all bright with gold. Mindful of courtesy, she brought a cup of mead to the noble guest.

Beowulf drained it. "When my warriors and I set out on the ocean," he said, "this was my thought—I would accomplish your people's desire or be destroyed in the grip of the fiend. I will do this deed or end my life here in this mead-hall."

At set of sun Hrothgar rose to leave the hall, and all the warriors followed.

"Never before did I entrust this noble Dane-hall to a stranger," the King said. "Guard it, Beowulf, keep it, watch for the foe. And if you come out of this battle alive, nothing you desire will be lacking to you."

BATTLE IN THE DARK

DARKNESS fell quickly. The Geats lay down on the hallbeds. There was not one who thought he would ever again see his homeland and folk. Yet all soon slept. Only the leader, wakeful and bold, awaited the battle.

Then, from the misty swampland, Grendel came. Under the dismal sky he stalked straight to Heorot. He struck open the iron-bolted portal and burst raging into the hall. His eyes gleamed like flame. He saw the hero-band clustered asleep, and his heart laughed that so lusty a banquet awaited his hunger.

At once the monster seized the nearest warrior and tore him fiercely asunder. He bit through the bones. He gulped the streaming blood. Greedily he swallowed the body piece by piece, devouring all, even the feet and hands. Then he moved on to the next. With fiendish claw he grasped the hero. But

Beowulf, eagerly waiting, clutched the monster boldly in return.

Such a hand grip Grendel had never felt before. His courage fled, he yearned for his lair. But up bounded Beowulf, mindful of his boast, and fiercely grasped his foe. The fiend's fingers cracked, his grip unloosed. He made off toward the door, but Beowulf followed close. Then din filled the mead-hall. Benches tumbled, ale was spilt, the house resounded while the grim foes wrestled. Grendel shrieked and groaned. A wonder it was that the hall stood firm!

The thanes had leaped from their beds, and now many a one brandished his blade to shield his lord's life, not knowing that the keenest of swords could do no harm to Grendel—by his spells he was safe from the iron's edge. Yet he who had done so many murders soon found that his body-frame failed him now. A monstrous wound showed on his shoulder. The tendons ripped, the bone-frame burst.

The fiend knew well that the wound was mortal. With a hideous cry he tore himself out of the hero's grasp and fled to his den.

Beowulf did not try to follow. What need? In his hand was proof that he had made good his boast. Down under the gabled roof he laid a bloody trophy—shoulder, arm and hand—all, indeed, of Grendel's grip.

AFTER THE BATTLE, GLORY

WHEN morning came, warriors from near and far gathered to view the wonder. Some eagerly traced to the lair the weary-hearted footsteps of Grendel. Death-marked he had fled to the lake. That was easy to see from the waters, how they seethed and boiled with his hot blood.

From that merry journey the clansmen raced home, shouting aloud their praise:

"None is more valiant than Beowulf! From sea to sea, from north to south, no man under the arching heavens is more worthy to rule!"

The morning sun was climbing high when they returned to the hall. The King himself with his retinue had come out to gaze at the trophy, and with him the Queen and her maidens. They stood by the steps, staring upward, wonder-struck. From the steep roof above, Grendel's hideous hand hung down.

"Let thanks be given to Almighty God for this sight!" the King exclaimed. "How many sorrows I have endured from Grendel! I had lost hope that the fiend would be stopped. But now this hero, with God's help, has done what all of us could not do. Beowulf, best of warriors, I shall love you as my own son. You shall never lack wealth as long as I have it."

All warm with the praise, Beowulf answered, "We fought this fight most willingly. I wish, though, you might gaze rather at the fiend's body itself. I meant to bind him down so that he should breathe his last in my hand. But his body slipped away."

All looked on the iron claws of Grendel and could not look away.

Afterwards, throngs of men and women hastened to cleanse the hall and deck it for feasting. Gold-worked tapestries were hung on the walls. And when all was ready, the King went to the hall.

Then Hrothgar gave costly gifts to the hero: a gold-woven battle flag, a breastplate and helmet richly adorned, and a splendid sword. Next, eight swift horses with gold-inlaid head-trappings were led into the hall, among them the King's own battle-mount with jewelled saddle.

"I wish you joy, dearest Beowulf, of these steeds and their trappings," Hrothgar said.

Nor did he forget the hero-band. To each of the companions who had followed Beowulf over the sea, he gave a costly gift. And for him whom Grendel had murdered, the King bade recompense to be paid in gold.

Afterwards the harp was plucked and Hrothgar's glee-man sang a hero-lay. Cup-bearers drew wine from the great vats. Glad voices sounded along the ale-benches and laughter rang out. It was the best of feasts.

That night another lodging was prepared for the Geats, and the hall was guarded, as once it had been, by a troop of Danish warriors. They cleared the benches and spread beds and bolsters. At their heads they set their shields, their armor, and weapons. Ever ready for battle were these thanes. Whether at home or raiding the coasts, they were prepared to defend their King. They were excellent men.

GRENDEL'S MOTHER

MEANTIME, in the dreary swampland, Grendel's mother had mourned her son, brooding on vengeance. At dark she stalked to Heorot. Raging, she burst open the door.

Up then sprang the warriors, swords drawn, shields firmly held. When she saw them around her, the woman-monster took fright. Less grim than Grendel, she fled

from the hall, yet not so fast but that she left woe behind. With one hand she snatched up a warrior, with the other tore Grendel's arm from the gable, and went off with the booty.

"Send for Beowulf!" the King commanded when news of the raid was brought to him.

It was dawn. The hero came, his band

about him. "I trust that the King passed the night in peace?" he said.

"Ask me not about pleasure!" Hrothgar wailed. "Pain has returned to Danish folk. Aeschere is dead, my sage adviser, my dearest thane. Here in Heorot a hand has slain and carried him off, I know not whither. You killed Grendel. Now another comes to avenge her kin. Men who live by the lake have said that sometimes they have seen a monster pair haunting the swampland, and one was a woman. There at night weird fire glows on the waters. None of the sons of men have plumbed their depth. Now, Beowulf, once more you alone can help. Seek this creature if you dare! And if you come back from that fight, I will reward you with ancient treasure."

"Grieve not," Beowulf said. "It is better to avenge a friend than fruitlessly to mourn him. Let us ride at once and follow the trail. I promise you, flee where she will, no retreat will hide her, neither the depths of the earth nor the forested mountain nor the floor of the sea."

The old chief leaped up. "Let horses be saddled!" he said.

THE MONSTER'S LAIR

HROTHGAR rode ahead, his henchmen followed. Over steep cliffs they went, and narrow passages, sheer headlands and unknown ways, wherever the footprints led. At last they came to a forested hill. Below, the waves of the lake were dyed with gore. And there on the shore lay Aeschere's head—a sight hard to behold.

Then battle horns sounded, and the shield-troop halted. On the water they saw worm-like creatures crawling and strange sea-dragons swimming about. Monsters lay on the cliffs, sea snakes and nicors sunned themselves. When they heard the battle horns blowing, they savagely started away. But Beowulf was undismayed as he girded himself for battle.

"Remember now your promise, wise sovereign," he said. "If I lose my life in your cause, you must mourn me as a father. Watch over my thanes. And the goodly gifts you gave me, send to Hygelac."

So saying, the hero plunged into the waters and let them close over him. An hour passed before he felt the floor of the lake. Down below, the sea-wolf awaited him— well she knew that some man was seeking to raid her monster-realm. With grisly claw she clutched the warrior and bore him away to her den, while he vainly strove to strike at the tusked sea beasts that swarmed around and tore at his mail.

All at once Beowulf found himself in a hall shut away from the water. A fire burned there, and by its light he saw the monster-woman. He swung his mighty sword and brought it down on her head. But the blade refused to bite.

"To my hand grip alone I will trust," he thought. Flinging the sword away, he seized the monster by the shoulder and threw her on the ground. She repaid him swiftly, grappling with such strength that Beowulf stumbled and fell. At that she hurled herself on him and drew her short sword. Had his breastplate not withstood the blade, life would have ended for the hero; the Geat would have perished.

But now he summoned his strength. He thrust her off and stood erect. At the same moment, on the wall of that den he saw a matchless blade. It was an ancient warriors' sword, wrought by giants of old, so heavy a weapon that no ordinary man could wield it. Beowulf seized it by the chain-hilt and swung the blade. He struck such a blow that it broke through the bone-rings of the monster's neck. And she sank in her death agony to the floor.

Suddenly light blazed forth. It was as bright there as if the sun were shining. Beowulf looked around and saw that Grendel's body lay by the wall. The hero raised his weapon and with a savage blow severed the horrible head.

Up above, the Danes who waited with Hrothgar looked aghast on the tossing waves as they saw them grow bloody.

"The hero has been slain," they said with sorrow. "Beowulf will not come again to seek our mighty King."

Hrothgar bowed his head. He turned his horse toward home, and all the noble Danes followed him. Only the Geats stayed on. Sick at heart, they stared at the gory waves, doubting, yet longing, to see their brave leader once again.

BEOWULF'S TRIUMPH

Down under the lake, Beowulf looked with amazement at the mighty sword in his hand. The ancient war-blade was melting as icicles melt in the spring! Burned was the bright sword, dissolved by the hot blood of the mother-monster. Only the hilt, blazing with jewels, was left in his hand. Beowulf saw many precious things in that den, but only the hilt he took with him as upward he swam through the waters.

"God be thanked!" the Geats cried when their leader reached the shore. "Little we thought to see you again alive!"

They stripped off his helmet and breastplate. Then, hearts full of gladness, by many a footpath and road they went back to Heorot, fourteen Geats marching, with

Grendel's head on a spear carried by four of them.

Awe fell on the henchmen when Beowulf entered the mead-hall. And when after him the monster head was borne in by the hair, the King and Queen sat speechless.

"Lo, mighty King!" Beowulf said. "This sea-booty we have brought you! The crimes are avenged. You can sleep safe in Heorot now, you and your thanes."

"Beowulf, my friend, dearest and best of men," Hrothgar said when he could speak, "far and wide your fame must fly! Heaven be thanked that after long evil my eyes at last gaze on this head, all hewn and bloody. Go now to the bench! Worthy warrior, rejoice at the banquet, be glad! At dawn of day a wealth of treasure shall be yours."

THE PARTING

THE MORNING shone bright as Beowulf went to the King. "Lo," he said, "the time has come to say we are departing. We have found here unfailing hosts, but now we would seek Hygelac. If ever on this earth I can win more of your love than I have done already, I will gladly do it. Should it come to my ears that your neighbors threaten you with terror, I will quickly come to your side with thousands of thanes. Hygelac, I know, will lend you help. And if your son should come to the court of the Geats, he will find friends."

"Loved Beowulf," Hrothgar answered, "you are as wise in words as you are strong in hand and wary in mind. If ever it happens that Hygelac falls by sword in battle, and you still live, the Geats will find no better man to choose for their king. You have brought our two peoples together. As long as I live, let us greet one another with tokens of love."

Twelve treasures then Hrothgar gave the hero. "Take them," he said, "to the folk you love, and come back soon."

With that the King kissed Beowulf and fell on his neck while tears flowed fast from the old man's eyes. "I am old," he thought. "My days on earth are few. It is unlikely that I will look on the hero again."

THE FIRE-DRAGON

FAR-FAMED was Beowulf after that bold venture in the land of the Danes. In many a mead-hall the lay was sung how with mighty grip the hero had slain the hater of men, then afterwards killed the mother of Grendel. And when in after years Hygelac fell in a raid and his son perished by sword of war, Beowulf came to rule the broad realm.

He ruled it wisely for fifty years. Then terror came to the Geats as terror had come to the Danes. In the dark of night, a dragon began to rage. A thief had stolen a goblet from the dragon's golden hoard, and now for the sin of one, prince and people must pay.

Where had that hoard of gold come from? Who had buried it in the stone barrow on the hill?

He who had hidden the gold was the last of his clan. He was left all alone to weep for his friends. Yet he would not give his gold away but stowed the treasure in the newly made grave of his kin, and covered it well.

When he, too, was dead, the dragon came to guard the gold. Three hundred winters he guarded it. And no man knew it was there. Then the thief came and aroused the dragon's wrath—a desperate man he was, fleeing from his angry lord. He came on the hoard by chance.

"This goblet," he thought, "will win me my pardon." And he stole the vessel and laid it at his Prince's feet.

The Dragon knew when he awoke that a man had been near. He snuffed around the cliff, greedy to find the evildoer. But none was there. He entered the barrow and saw that the cup was gone. He waited, raging, until evening, then flew, folded in flame, to take revenge on the sons of men. The fiend belched fire. The homes of the Geats blazed. All living things in the monster's path were wrapped in flame. Not until dawn did the destroyer return to the barrow.

FOR THE LAST TIME

BEOWULF'S own house had gone up in flames. So had the stronghold on the shore. It was heavy sorrow for the old King.

"I will go forth once more," he said. "But wooden shield against fire is worthless."

He bade his smiths make him a shield all of iron. Then he chose eleven comrades and went to seek the dragon. With them went a thirteenth man—he who was the cause of all this strife, he who had stolen the cup. He led them straight to the barrow by the sea.

The old hero King sat down on the headland.

"Through many wars have I lived," he said. "Now once again I will seek to do a mighty deed. I shall not retreat a step from the guardian of this barrow. One fight shall end all. Now wait for me by the barrow, wait till the end. The iron shield will stand against the dragon's fire!"

With this he rose and went beneath the overhanging rock. Soon by the wall he saw a stone arch and within it a stream, boiling hot. That way he could never hope to reach the treasure unharmed. So he raised a shout, and the dragon came rushing to the strife, pouring his poison-breath before him.

Sword drawn, shield held high, the King stood stoutly awaiting the attack. The blazing serpent glided toward him. Beowulf lifted his arm and struck the foul worm with his weapon. It was a heavy blow, but the edge of the sword was turned.

The dragon was wild with pain. He cast fire all about him. He made such din that the men outside fled to the woods in terror. Then once more he closed with his foe and enfolded the hero in flames.

But now through the hideous din, Beowulf heard a voice: "Beowulf! King! Fight with all your strength! I come to stand at your side!"

It was young Wiglaf who spoke. Alone of the chosen comrades he had dared go to his chieftain's help.

At his words the dragon attacked. He was mad with rage. The flames flared forth, consuming Wiglaf's wooden shield, but the young thane quickly went under Beowulf's shield of iron. And now again the King struck—a heavier blow than the first, a blow of hate that drove into the dragon's head and shattered the sword. The fiend recoiled. Then for the third time he rushed. The poisonous teeth closed on Beowulf's neck, and waves of blood welled from his breast.

Wiglaf's arm was burned, but he paid no heed to the loathsome head. Underneath the awful jaws he drove his gleaming sword, and at once the fire began to lessen and wane. Then Beowulf summoned his failing senses. He drew the dagger he wore on his corselet, and with a final effort slit the dragon in two.

DEATH OF A HERO

For Beowulf this was the last deed of valor, the last triumph. Already the terrible wound had begun to swell and smart, and soon the pain of poison filled his breast. Stumbling on to the rock wall, he sank down. His henchman washed away the blood and unlaced his helmet.

"Had I a son," Beowulf said, for he knew his wound was mortal, "I would now give him this war gear. . . . Fifty winters I have ruled this people. All that time, no king dared to wage war on me or threaten me with terror. I waited at home for what fate might bring, took care of what was mine. I sought no feuds. I never falsely swore an oath. And because of these things, I die in gladness. Now go quickly, loved Wiglaf, and find that hoard under the rock. I would behold the golden treasure and have joy in the gems. Then I would more easily lay down my life and kingship I have so long held."

The warrior went. He saw glittering jewels lying on the ground. By the wall was many a marvelous vessel and weapon. He saw golden bowls, and ancient rusty helmets, and arm rings wondrously twisted. And over the hoard was a gold-woven banner. Wiglaf burdened his arms with goblets and plates and took also that gold-woven banner. Then he hastily retraced his steps, doubting if he would find his lord alive.

The King lay bleeding heavily. He was at the end of life. His kinsman splashed him with water again, and Beowulf stared at the sight of all the gold.

"For what I behold I give thanks to God," he said. "Thanks that I have been able to give to my folk such gifts before the day of my death has run out. I have bartered the last of my life for treasure. Now I need tarry no longer. Bid my warriors raise a burial mound for my ashes high on Hrones-Headland, that seafarers, homeward returning, may often hail it and say, 'There is Beowulf's Barrow.'"

He spoke, and unclasping the golden chain from his neck, gave it to his kinsman, together with breastplate and ring. "Use them in joy," he said. "You are the last of our race. Fate has swept away all the rest of my line. I go now to join them."

Beowulf spoke no more, and death flowed over him.

And now came the laggards who had fled to the wood. In shame they carried their shields. They gazed on Wiglaf where he sat trying to revive Beowulf with water, and Wiglaf looked back at them, sad at heart.

"The King who gave you the armor you stand in," he said, "wasted it, threw it away. He had no reason to boast of his friends in the fight. But God gave him strength to get his revenge alone. It was little I could do to help him, yet I tried. Too few were around him in the hour of need. And now you will lose all he gave you. When lords afar hear of your shameful flight, they will come and take away your treasure and the joy of home and your land. Death is better than life stained by shame!"

BEOWULF'S BARROW

All morning long at the stronghold on the cliff, the thanes had sat waiting in sorrow. Would they bewail or welcome home their dear lord? But now all was known. The messenger who had ridden up the headland had returned and told the sorrowful tidings, withholding nothing.

The warriors climbed up the cliff. There on the earth was the giver of rings, and Wiglaf keeping a death watch beside him. There the fiery dragon lay—fifty feet long by measure. And there was the treasure.

Wiglaf spoke. "This hoard is ours," he said, "but grievously got. He would not take our counsel, our beloved King, when we urged that he should not grapple with the guardian of gold. . . . He was the noblest warrior the wide earth over. . . . But now let a bier be made so that we may carry this beloved man to Hrones-Ness, for it is there he commanded we build his barrow. Now I will show you the way to the treasure."

Then Wiglaf chose seven thanes, the best in the band, to go with him into the cave. They hauled out the treasure—countless it was—and laid the gold on a wagon. The hated dragon they cast over the wall for the waves to take. And the King they bore to Hrones-Ness.

To that headland firewood was brought from homesteads near and far, and the Geat folk built Beowulf a funeral-pile. They hung it around with helmets and breastplates. In the midst of the armor they laid the chieftain. Then wood-smoke rose on the hill and fires leaped to the heavens, while weeping mingled with the roar of the flames.

There on the headland in ten days' time they fashioned a barrow broad and high. Far out on the water, seafarers could see it. Around the brands of the fire they built a wall. And in that barrow they placed the precious treasure they had taken from the hoard, gold as useless to men now as it was before.

Then a band of twelve nobles rode around the barrow, making lament for their King:

"Of all the kings of earth, he was the mildest and most beloved, to his kin the kindest."

Thus they chanted their dirge. Thus the men of Geatland mourned the passing of their hero.

THE BATTLE OF RONCEVAUX

THE GUILE OF BLANCANDRIN

For seven years Charlemagne had waged war against the Moors in Spain. Now all was conquered to the sea. No castle or city or wall remained to be battered down but noble Saragossa, standing on a mountain. Proud King Marsile held the city, and he was hard pressed.

He went into an orchard, and reclining on a bench of blue marble, spoke to his dukes and his counts:

"Misfortune, my lords, overwhelms us. I have no such army as can give Charles battle and destroy his forces. So counsel me, wise men that you are, and save me from death and shame."

Not one of the Pagans replied except Blancandrin, wisest among the Saracens.

"Do not be dismayed," he said. "Pretend to submit. Send proud Charlemagne promises of faithful service and deep friendship. Give him rich gifts. Say that at Michaelmas you will come and be baptized and become

his vassal. If he demands hostages, give him ten or twenty. Send him our sons. I will be the first to give up mine. Then Charlemagne will go back to France."

"It may well be so!" the nobles said.

"By this beard that ripples on my breast," Blancandrin went on, "you will see the French army disbanded. Once they return to France and the King is at Aix, each will go to his own domain. The appointed time will pass and Charles will hear no word of us. He is proud. He will cut off the heads of our sons. But better that than that we should lose bright Spain and dignity and honor, and have to beg our bread."

King Marsile thought over Blancandrin's words. Then he chose ten noble lords.

"Go to Charlemagne at Cordova," he said. "Bear olive branches in your hands. Assure him that in a month's time I will receive baptism and become his vassal. If he demands hostages, he shall have them."

"WHOM SHALL WE SEND TO SARAGOSSA?"

THE EMPEROR CHARLES sat under a pine tree in captured Cordova and held council with his barons. He had heard King Marsile's messengers. Now he wished to follow the advice of the nobles of France.

"Noble lords," he said, "the Pagan Marsile promises to give me great wealth if I will return to France. He will send me bears, lions, and greyhounds on the leash, seven hundred camels, a thousand falcons, four hundred mules laden with gold, and fifty wagons. He himself will follow me to Aix and there receive our holy faith. He will be my vassal and hold Spain of me. So he says, but I know not what he truly intends."

"We had better beware!" the nobles said.

"Yes, beware!" Charlemagne's loved nephew, Count Roland spoke up. "It would be foolish to trust Marsile. He deceived you before. Seven years ago, when we came to Spain, he sent you messengers. They spoke to you these very same words. You sent him two of your counts to make terms. And he took off their heads! No, say I. Carry on this war. Lead us to Saragossa and lay siege to the city even if it takes the rest of your life.

Avenge Basan and Basile whom the traitor put to death!"

The Emperor was silent. So were the nobles—all but Ganelon. He sprang to his feet.

"He who counsels you to reject the offer of King Marsile," he said, "does not care in the least what death we die. He speaks out of foolish pride. Let us have done with fools!" And he glared at Roland, his stepson, with hate.

Duke Naimes spoke. "There is wisdom in Ganelon's words," he said. "You have vanquished King Marsile. When he asks you for mercy and offers to give you hostages, it would be a grievous sin to carry on the war any longer."

"The Duke is right," the others agreed.

"Whom, then, shall we send to Saragossa to King Marsile?" Charlemagne asked.

"I will go, with your permission," Duke Naimes said. "Give me the glove and the staff."

"No, you are my councillor. By my beard and my moustache," said Charles, "you shall not go so far from me now. Go and sit down —no one is calling on you."

"I myself can very well go," Roland said.

"Indeed, no," his good friend Oliver objected. "Your temper is short and you are proud. I am afraid you will get into trouble. If the King wishes it, I will go."

"Be quiet, both of you!" said Charles. "Neither you nor Roland nor any one of the Twelve Peers shall go."

Archbishop Turpin of Rheims stood up. "Let me go to the Saracen, Sire," he said.

The Emperor frowned. "Go and sit down!" he commanded. "Let me hear no more about it from you." Then turning to the knights, he said, "Choose me a baron to bear my message to Marsile."

"Send Ganelon, who is my stepfather," Roland said.

"He will do well," said the French. "None would be more prudent."

Ganelon was furious. He flung his great sables from his shoulders and stood there in his silken tunic. His eyes were blazing.

"Fool!" he said to Roland. "Why have you chosen me who am your stepfather? If God grants that I come back, I will make such trouble for you that it will last you for a lifetime."

"I pay no attention to threats," Roland answered. "I chose you because an ambassador must be a wise man. I am ready to go in your place."

"You are not my vassal," Ganelon said. "Since Charles commands me, I will go to Marsile. But I promise you I shall do something or other to soothe my anger!"

Roland began to laugh, and at that Ganelon nearly lost his reason. "I have no love for you!" he shouted.

Then he addressed Charlemagne: "Just Emperor, here I am. I am ready to do your will. I know well that he who goes to Saragossa cannot return. I ask you, therefore, to take care of my son, your sister's child; for I shall never again set eyes on him."

"Ganelon," the Emperor said, "the French have chosen you; so you must go. Come forward and receive the staff and the glove."

Ganelon stepped forward and took them. "Sire," he said, "all this is Roland's doing. As long as I live I shall never love him, nor Oliver his comrade, nor the Twelve Peers because they are so fond of Roland. I defy them all!"

"Your anger is too great," the King said.

"Perhaps. But remember that Basile and his brother Basan did not return."

GANELON'S TREASON

GANELON rode toward Saragossa side by side with Blancandrin, who had come with the messengers of King Marsile. The wily Saracen had sensed that the Frenchman was in a smoldering rage and ever so softly sounded him out on Roland.

magne sends you this message: You must accept our holy faith. Then he will give you half of Spain to hold as his vassal. If you refuse these terms, the Emperor will besiege you in Saragossa. You shall be taken by force and brought to Aix where you will be con-

"He is the Emperor's darling," Ganelon said with bitterness. "Roland flings himself at death in order to lay kings' crowns at his uncle's feet. And the French all love him, for the Count showers gold and silver on them, mules and coursers, silks and clothing. They will fail him in nothing. As long as Roland lives there will be no peace—he will conquer for Charles all the lands from here to the Orient."

Blancandrin saw that Ganelon was ripe for treachery. With great guile he talked to the Frenchman, and they came to an understanding. Ganelon would betray the French. He would take Saracen gold and work out a plan to slay Roland. Then hand in hand the two went before Marsile.

Said Blancandrin, "We delivered your message to Charles. He sends you his noble baron, from whom you will learn whether or not you shall have peace."

"Let him speak!" the King commanded.

"God save you!" Ganelon said. "Charle-

demned to death and die in shame and dishonor. Our Emperor sends you this." And he placed a letter in Marsile's hand.

Marsile broke the seal. As he read the letter, his face grew red, then pale.

"Charles tells me," he said to his nobles, "to remember his wrath about Basan and his brother Basile, whose heads I cut off. He says that if I wish to purchase my life, I must send him my uncle the Caliph. Otherwise I shall not have his friendship."

"Ganelon has gone too far!" Marsile's son cried out in fury. "Hand him over to me! I will do justice by him!"

Ganelon drew his sword. But Blancandrin made a sign to him and at the same time said to the King, "He has pledged me his word that he will work for us."

The King was startled. His expression changed.

"Sir Ganelon," he said, "I can raise an army of four hundred thousand knights. Can I stand off Charles with that many?"

"Do not attempt it," Ganelon said. "Let wisdom guide you. Send him so much wealth that every Frenchman will be astonished by it. If you send him also twenty hostages, he will return to France, leaving a rear guard of twenty thousand men. His nephew, Count Roland, who is Charlemagne's right hand, and Oliver the Brave will be among them and the Twelve Peers who love him so well. If you follow my advice, the two counts will be dead men. The flower of Charles' army will fall, and he will never make war on you again."

"Fair Sir Ganelon," Marsile said, "how can I bring about the death of Roland?"

"Send a hundred thousand men to attack the rear guard in the pass of Cize, which Charles will take to go into France," Ganelon said. "Follow up the first battle with a second, and from one or the other of them Roland will not escape."

At these words the Saracen embraced Ganelon. "Give me your word that you will betray Roland," Marsile said.

He held out his sword. And on the holy relics in the sword hilt, Ganelon swore treason.

Afterwards Marsile said to him, "Take care not to break your oath, and every year you shall have ten mules laden with the finest gold of Araby. But here now are the keys of Saragossa. Present them to King Charles. Contrive to have Roland in the rear guard, and I will give him battle to the death."

"TWENTY THOUSAND FRANKS WILL BE ENOUGH!"

THE EMPEROR stood on the green grass before his tent with Roland and Oliver, the Duke Naimes and many others, waiting for Ganelon and tribute from the land of Spain. At last they saw the traitor coming.

"God save you!" Ganelon said, speaking with great guile. "I bring you the keys of Saragossa, enormous riches, and twenty hostages. Marsile the Noble asks you to pardon him for not surrendering the Caliph. I saw with my own eyes how he fled to the sea with three hundred thousand men, for they would not accept our Christian faith. As for the King, before a month ends he will follow you to France, be baptized, and become your vassal."

"God be praised!" the Emperor cried. "Now we will take our way to France! Let the trumpets blow!"

High were the peaks, black the rocks, monstrous the shadows. Charlemagne saw the pass and the narrow defiles, and he said to his nobles:

"Choose for me the leader of the rear guard."

Quickly Ganelon spoke up. "Let it be Roland, my stepson. There is no other baron of such prowess in your entire Kingdom."

"You are mad!" the King cried. "If Roland stays behind, who will lead the vanguard in front of me?"

"Ogier of Denmark," Ganelon said. "None could do it better."

"Sire," said Roland, "I have cause to love my stepfather well for having named me for the rear guard. I promise you that neither palfrey nor charger, neither mule nor ass will be lost unless it dearly be purchased by the sword."

The Emperor bowed his head, for he could not keep back his tears. After a time he said:

"Fair Sir Nephew, I will leave you half my army."

"That I will never accept!" Roland cried. "I will not disgrace my kin! Twenty thousand valiant Franks will be enough. You may confidently go through the pass. As long as I am alive, you need fear no man."

His comrade Oliver came to Roland's side. Gerin and brave Count Gerier joined them, Archbishop Turpin and Count Walter de l'Hum. Among them they chose twenty thousand knights. Fearless and unmindful of death, they stood by and watched the French enter the pass.

"ROLAND, MY COMRADE, BLOW YOUR HORN"

MEANTIME the Saracens were riding out from Saragossa to attack Roland at Roncevaux. Their triple-thick coats of mail glistened in the sun. Saragossa helmets were on their heads. Fair shields and lances from Valencia were in their hands. White, blue, and crimson pennants streamed from the points of their lances. And all up and down the ranks two words resounded— "Roland" and "Roncevaux."

Charlemagne had long passed out of sight. He was already nearing the frontier of France when the sound of Saracen trumpets suddenly broke on the ears of the rear guard.

"Roland," said Oliver, "it looks as if we may do battle with the Saracens!"

"God grant that we may!" Roland replied. "We will make a stand here for our King."

Oliver left Roland and climbed up a hill. Then he saw the Pagan army advancing, host on host.

"Roland!" he called out. "What a glitter of armor I see, what a flash of coats of mail and flaming helmets! Ganelon—that traitor —has sold us!"

"Be quiet, Oliver," Roland replied. "He is my stepfather. I will not have you say a word against him!"

Oliver looked at the Saracen army and was filled with dismay. It seemed to him the troops were without number. Quickly he ran down the hill to tell the French what he had seen.

"There are a hundred thousand of the Pagans in the forefront," he said. "You will have such a battle as never was. Stand firm, nobles of France!"

"We shall not fail you!" the French replied stoutly.

"Roland," Oliver said, "the Pagan forces are immense, and it seems to me we are too few for them. Blow your horn! Charlemagne will hear it and bring the army back."

"That would be foolish!" Roland answered. "I would lose my honor. I promise you, the Pagans are all doomed to die."

"Roland, my comrade, blow your horn!" Oliver pleaded. "The King will come with his barons to help us."

"God forbid," Roland replied, "that my kin should be shamed because of me, and sweet France come to be despised. I promise you the Saracens shall all be slain."

But still Oliver implored. "Roland, my comrade, blow your horn! I see no dishonor in what I ask. The valleys and the mountains are covered with the Saracens, and our army is very small indeed."

"God and the holy angels forbid that France should lose her glory on account of me! We shall stand our ground. There is not a coward among us."

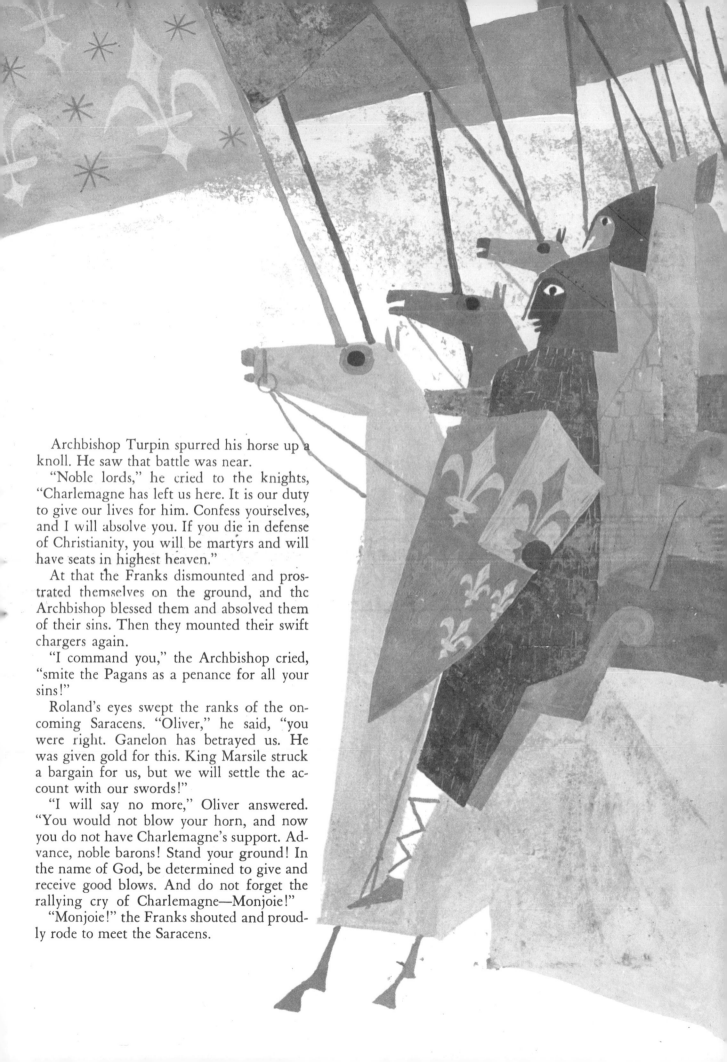

Archbishop Turpin spurred his horse up a knoll. He saw that battle was near.

"Noble lords," he cried to the knights, "Charlemagne has left us here. It is our duty to give our lives for him. Confess yourselves, and I will absolve you. If you die in defense of Christianity, you will be martyrs and will have seats in highest heaven."

At that the Franks dismounted and prostrated themselves on the ground, and the Archbishop blessed them and absolved them of their sins. Then they mounted their swift chargers again.

"I command you," the Archbishop cried, "smite the Pagans as a penance for all your sins!"

Roland's eyes swept the ranks of the oncoming Saracens. "Oliver," he said, "you were right. Ganelon has betrayed us. He was given gold for this. King Marsile struck a bargain for us, but we will settle the account with our swords!"

"I will say no more," Oliver answered. "You would not blow your horn, and now you do not have Charlemagne's support. Advance, noble barons! Stand your ground! In the name of God, be determined to give and receive good blows. And do not forget the rallying cry of Charlemagne—Monjoie!"

"Monjoie!" the Franks shouted and proudly rode to meet the Saracens.

CHRISTIANS VERSUS PAGANS

Roland rode in front, mounted on his good steed Veillantif. He carried his weapons gracefully and advanced toying with his lance, twirling it. From the tip of the lance hung his all-white pennant, its golden fringes beating against his hands. His figure was noble, his face bright and laughing. His comrade Oliver followed close behind. Roland looked haughtily at the Saracens but turned a gentle eye on the French.

"Noble lords, advance with confidence," he said. "These Pagans are looking for death. Today we are going to take fine booty— never did a king of France win so much."

The Saracens were confident too. Aelroth, Marsile's nephew, advanced alone in front of the troops.

"Villainous Frenchmen!" he shouted insultingly. "Today you are going to do battle with us. He who should have defended you has betrayed you. Your King was mad to leave you in this pass. Today France will lose her renown and Charlemagne his right arm from his body!"

When Roland heard him, he was enraged. He spurred his horse and rode as hard as he could to smite the Pagan. He pierced his shield and tore his coat of mail, cut open his breast, and broke his bones. He severed his spine and flung him dead from his horse.

"There you are, villain!" Roland cried. "Charlemagne is not a madman and never loved treachery. In leaving us at the pass he acted as a brave man should, and sweet France will not lose her glory today. Strike, Franks! The first blow is ours! Right is on our side!"

Bitter was the rage of the Saracens when

they saw Aelroth fall. Falsaron, King Marsile's brother, charged from the press. He shouted the Pagan battle-cry and taunted the French.

"Today sweet France shall lose her honor!" he cried.

Oliver was seized with fury. He spurred his horse and attacked the Saracen in knightly fashion. He pierced the Pagan's shield, rent the coat of mail, and with the full force of his lance struck him from the saddle—dead.

"Strike, Franks," Oliver said, "and victory will be ours! Monjoie!"

There was a Saracen king there, Corsablis by name. He was from Barbary, a far-off land. Pagan words fell from his tongue.

"Saracens," he cried, "the French are few in number, and Charles will not save a single one of them. This is the day of their death!"

Archbishop Turpin heard him. There was no one under heaven whom he hated so much as this Pagan. He spurred his horse and rode straight at him. He broke the Pagan's shield in pieces, rent his coat of mail, and with the full force of his lance thrust him down dead upon the ground. Turpin looked at the body stretched on the earth and said," Cowardly Pagan, you lied. Charlemagne my lord is always our support, and we French have no talent for fleeing. Strike, Franks! Show your lances! This first blow is ours, praise God! Monjoie!"

The battle joined. The French were marvelous everywhere. Count Roland thrust with his lance as long as the shaft lasted. But at the fifteenth blow it broke in pieces. Then he drew out Durendal, his good sword which the Emperor had given him, and flung himself on the enemy, crying:

"Scoundrels! To your sorrow you came here. Your Mahomet will not save you!"

He rode across the field of battle, doing great slaughter with Durendal. He piled the dead one on another and the bright blood flowed. His coat of mail and his arms were all bloody. So were the neck and shoulders of his good steed. As for Oliver, he did not hang back. Nor could anybody find fault with the Twelve Peers. The French struck right and left, and the Pagans died on every hand.

"Long live our barons!" cried the Archbishop. "Monjoie!"

Oliver rode through the press. His lance was broken, and only the stump remained.

"What are you doing, comrade?" Roland cried. "Of what use is a stick in a battle like this? Where is your sword Hauteclaire with its golden hilt and crystal pommel?"

"I cannot draw it; I am too busy striking!" Oliver replied.

The battle meantime had stiffened. How many lances were bloody and broken! How many flags and standards were in rags! How many good Franks were killed in the flower of their youth, who would nevermore see their mothers or their wives or their friends waiting for them! How badly Ganelon served his lord that day when he went to sell his own people to Saragossa! But on that account he would lose both life and limb. For the court of Aix would condemn him to be hanged, and along with him thirty of his closest kin.

The battle was fierce and grim. Oliver and Roland struck marvelously, and the Archbishop gave blows by the thousand. The Twelve Peers did not hang back. By hundreds, by thousands, the Pagans fell, and he who did not flee did not escape death.

But now Marsile advanced with his second army. He saw the slaughter of the first and commanded his horns and trumpets to be blown for the charge.

"Brother Oliver, my comrade," cried Ro-

land when he heard the sound and saw the fields all around covered with Pagans. "The traitor Ganelon has sworn our death. But the Emperor will take a terrible revenge."

The Archbishop rallied the barons. "No cowardly thoughts now! In God's name, do not flee—better to die fighting. It is our fate to end here today, but I promise you one thing: holy Paradise awaits you, and you will be among the saints."

"Monjoie!" the French shouted.

The battle was marvelous and mighty. The French struck with vigor and rage. They severed hands, spines, and pierced armor to the living flesh. The bright blood rolled on the green grass. Roland and Oliver smote and hewed with their swords. The Archbishop struck with his lance. Between them they smote down more than four thousand.

All went well for the French in the first four attacks, but the fifth was cruel and fatal to them. All the French knights lay dead on the field of battle except sixty whom God had spared. But those sixty, before dying, would sell themselves dear.

ROLAND BLOWS HIS HORN

OUNT ROLAND saw the great losses among his men and called his comrade Oliver.

"Alas that the King is not here!" Count Roland said. "Oliver my brother, how can we let him know the news?"

"I know no way," said Oliver. "I would rather die than be dishonored."

"Ah," said Roland, "I will blow my horn. Charles will hear it as he crosses the pass, and the French will return."

"That would be very shameful now," Oliver said, "and would dishonor all your kin. All their life they would have to blush for it. By my beard, if ever I see Aude, my noble sister, again, you shall not be her husband!"

"Why this anger?" Roland asked.

"Friend," Oliver replied, "it is all your fault. When I begged you to blow your horn, you refused to do it. There lie our French, dead through your heedlessness. Ah, Roland, we may well mourn your prowess.

Charlemagne will not have you to help him any more, and to the last judgment there will never be another man like you. You are going to die, and France will be humbled. Today our loyal friendship will end. Before evening we shall have to part."

The Archbishop heard their dispute and spurred his horse. "In the name of God," he said, "stop your quarreling. Blowing the horn now will not help you. Still, it would be better to blow it and have the King come, for he could avenge us. These Spaniards must not go home rejoicing."

"Well said, Sire," Roland replied.

He put the horn to his mouth, took a deep breath, and blew with all his strength. The sound prolonged itself far away in the high mountains. More than thirty leagues away the echo could be heard. Charlemagne heard it, and all his companions, too.

"Our men are doing battle," said the King.

Quickly Ganelon spoke up. "If anyone but you said it, it would be taken for a lie."

Roland blew his ivory horn again. He did it with such effort, such pain, that the bright blood gushed from his mouth and his temples burst.

Charles heard the echo as he crossed the pass. "I hear Roland's horn," he said. "He would certainly not sound it if he was not doing battle."

"There is no battle," Ganelon said. "You know how great is Roland's pride. It is a wonder that God has suffered it so long. Doubtless at this moment he is making merry—he will blow his horn all day after a hare he is hunting. Besides, who under heaven would dare attack him in the field?"

Count Roland's mouth was bloody and his temples had burst. With great pain and difficulty he blew his horn. Charlemagne and all the French heard it, and the King said, "This horn carries far."

The Duke Naimes answered, "It is because a good vassal is blowing it in distress. He who counsels you to pay no attention to it has betrayed Roland. Arm yourself! Give your war-cry and help your noble followers.

You can hear plainly that Roland is in deep despair."

The Emperor commanded his bugles to be blown. All the barons mounted their horses. As for Ganelon, the King had him seized at once and given into the keeping of his cooks.

High were the mountains, shadowy and immense, deep the valleys, swift the torrents. The clarions sounded in the van and in the rear, and all took up the call of Roland's horn. Not one of the French but wept and lamented and prayed God to keep Roland till they could join him on the field of battle. But what good? Alas! They were too late, they could not arrive in time.

THE PARTING

ROLAND looked around him at the mountains and plains. He saw the French dead on the field of battle and mourned them like a true knight.

"Noble barons, may God have pity on you! May he receive your souls into Paradise! Better warriors I have never seen. You, who have served me so long and have conquered so many lands! Ah, is it for this cruel end that the Emperor fostered you? And it is my fault that I see you die and can neither save nor defend you. May God help you, God who never deceives. Oliver my brother, I ought not to abandon you, but I shall die of grief if someone does not kill me. Let us go, comrade, let us go and strike again."

Roland returned to the battle. Never would there be a man more eager for revenge. As a stag flees before the hounds, so the Pagans fled before Roland.

"Strike," he cried, "and no quarter!"

At these words, the French took up the battle again, but there was great slaughter of Christians.

Marsile came on, mounted on his steed Gaignon. He dug in his spurs and rode to strike down Bevon de Beaume. He pierced his shield, tore his coat of mail, and struck him dead. Then he killed Ivoire and Ivon and Girard de Rousillon.

"May the good God confound you who

do me this great wrong!" Roland cried. "You shall know the name of my sword today!" With that he cut off Marsile's right hand. Then he cut off the head of Jurfaleu the Blond, King Marsile's son.

"Help us, Mahomet!" cried the Pagans in a panic. "Each man for himself!"

A hundred thousand fled. They would not return. But what did it matter? If Marsile fled, his uncle the Caliph remained. More than fifty thousand Ethiopians advanced with him.

When Roland saw them, he knew his comrades had not long to live.

"Strike, my lords, with your burnished swords!" he cried. "Do battle for your dead and for yourselves, and above all that sweet France may not be dishonored by us."

The Caliph spurred his red-brown horse and fell on Oliver and struck him from behind in the middle of the back. The Caliph thrust his lance clean through Oliver's breast.

"There," said he, "is a rugged blow for you! In you alone I have avenged my people!"

Oliver felt that he was wounded to death. Nevertheless he held his good sword Hauteclaire in his hand and struck the Caliph and split his head to the teeth.

"Curse you, Pagan!" he cried.

Oliver could not get his fill of revenge. He struck blow on blow, slashed lances and bucklers, feet and hands, shoulders and sides.

"Monjoie!" he shouted. Then he called Roland, his friend. "Comrade, come to my side, for today, alas, we shall be parted!"

Roland looked into Oliver's face. It had changed color, it was livid, discolored, pale. All down his body the bright blood flowed and great drops of it fell on the ground.

"O God!" Roland cried. "Now I know not what to do. Comrade, your courage has done you to death. Never will there be a man to equal you." And with this Roland swooned upon his horse.

Oliver had lost so much blood that he could not see clearly enough to recognize anyone far or near. He met his swooning comrade, struck him hard and clove his gilded helmet to the visor, but did not wound the head.

At this blow Roland came to himself. He looked at Oliver and asked gently and tenderly, "Comrade, did you mean to do it? This is Roland, who has loved you so. You have struck me without challenging me in any way."

"I hear you speak," Oliver said. "But I cannot see you at all—may God see you, friend! I struck you. Forgive me, I pray."

"I am not hurt," Roland said. "I forgive you here and before God."

They leaned towards each other and embraced with great love.

Oliver felt the approach of death. He dismounted, lay down on the ground and made confession. He raised his clasped hands to heaven and prayed God to give him Paradise, to bless Charlemagne, sweet France, and his comrade Roland above all men. His heart failed, his head bowed, he fell full length on the ground. The Count was dead. It was all over with Oliver. Brave Roland wept and mourned him.

"My comrade, we have been together many days, many years, and never have you done me any wrong, nor I you. Now that you are dead, all my grief is that I still live." With that the Count toppled over in a faint on his horse, Veillantif.

THE LAST ATTACK

WHEN ROLAND came to himself, he saw that great disaster had befallen the French. All were dead except the Archbishop and Walter de l'Hum.

"Where are you, noble Count?" he heard Walter calling. "Come to me. I have eight lance wounds in my body. I am going to die, but I will sell myself dear to the enemy."

Roland spurred his horse and galloped toward him. Together with the Archbishop they began to strike. Roland killed twenty Spaniards, Walter killed six, and the Archbishop killed five.

There were a thousand Pagans on foot

and forty thousand on horse—and not one dared approach the three Frenchmen. They sent their lances, javelins, darts, and arrows from afar. Walter was killed. Turpin de Rheims had four lance wounds in his body and his horse had been killed under him. He fell. But he was up in an instant and ran to Roland, crying out:

"I am not vanquished. A brave warrior never gives himself up alive."

He drew Almace, his sword of burnished steel, and struck in the thickest press. Four hundred dead were afterwards found close around him.

Roland fought bravely. But his whole body burned, he was drenched with sweat, and his head ached grievously, for in blowing the horn he had burst his temples. Still, he wanted to know if Charlemagne would come. So he seized his horn and drew a feeble sound from it.

At that sound Charlemagne stopped and listened. "My lords," he said, "it goes ill for us. Today we are going to lose my nephew Roland. We must press on. Let all the trumpets in the army be blown."

Sixty thousand horns resounded. Hearing that sound, the Pagans had no desire to laugh. "Charlemagne is coming!" they said. "If Roland remains alive, there will be war without end, and Spain is lost."

Four hundred of the best in the Pagan army came together to make an assault on Roland. When he saw them coming, he dug his golden spurs into Veillantif and sped to assail them all.

Then the Saracens cried one to another, "Let us flee, friends, for Charlemagne the Mighty is coming back and already we hear the cry 'Monjoie!' Count Roland has such proud courage that he will not let himself be conquered by mortal man. Let us take aim at him all together and leave him dead on the field."

A rain of darts, javelins, lances, and arrows fell on Roland. They pierced and broke his shield and tore his coat of mail, but they did not reach his body. His good charger Veillantif, wounded in thirty places, fell dead under the Count. But the Pagans fled and left Roland—alone and on foot.

He could not pursue them, for Veillantif was dead. He went to help the Archbishop, unlaced his helmet, took off his coat of mail, cut up his silken tunic, and stanched his great wounds. Then he pressed him to his heart and laid him down softly on the green grass.

"Noble lord, give me leave," he said. "We should not abandon our comrades whom we loved so much. I will go look for them and lay them by you."

"Go," said the Archbishop, "and come back soon. God be praised, you and I are masters of the field."

Roland went. He searched the valleys and mountains. He found ten of the Peers, carried them to the Archbishop, and laid them in a row before him.

"May the God of Glory receive all your souls," the Archbishop said, blessing and weeping over them. "I myself am in the anguish of death and will not see the noble Emperor."

Roland went again to search the field of battle. He finally found Oliver, bore him to the Archbishop, and laid him on a shield beside the others. Such was his grief that Roland fainted away. Then the Archbishop took Roland's horn and went to fill it with water for him. But he did not walk many steps before his heart failed and he fell heavily to the ground in the anguish of death.

THE DEATH OF ROLAND

WHEN ROLAND came to himself, he looked around and saw the Archbishop lying on the ground. He went up to him and crossed his hands on his breast.

"Alas!" the Count mourned, "since the holy Apostles there has been no such prophet. May your soul find the door of Paradise open!"

But now Roland himself felt death approaching. In one hand he took his horn, in the other his sword Durendal. He went into a fallow field where under two beautiful trees stood four blocks of cut marble.

High were the peaks, very high the trees, the four blocks of marble glistened. Roland looked at Durendal in his hand and his heart smote him. Before him was a brown rock. He struck ten blows upon it with Durendal, but he could not break the sword.

"Alas, Durendal, my good sword," he said, "you can no longer serve me. Yet I care for you no less. With you I have won so many pitched battles, conquered so many wide lands for Charlemagne of the White Beard. May no man capable of fleeing from another possess you! You have belonged to a good vassal a long time. There will never be his equal in France."

Then Roland struck on the block of marble. The steel grated, but neither broke nor chipped. When Roland saw that he could not break the sword, he lamented, "Ah, Durendal, how fair and bright you are, how you gleam and flame in the sun! It is better to die than leave you to the Pagans. God our father, spare France this shame!"

Roland struck the block of marble once again and broke off a great piece of it. The sword grated, but neither broke nor chipped.

"Ah, Durendal," he said, "how beautiful and holy you are! How many precious relics are in your golden hilt! A tooth of Saint Peter, blood of Saint Basil, hair of Saint Denis, a bit of the Virgin Mary's dress. It is not right for Pagans to possess you!"

Roland felt that death was taking hold of him. He ran and threw himself under a pine. And there, lying on the grass, his face against the earth and his sword and horn under him, he turned his head towards the Pagans. He did that so that Charlemagne and his whole army should say that he died conquering. He confessed his sins and as a token of his repentance held his right glove to God.

Roland felt that his time on earth was over. There on a peak he lay, his face turned toward Spain, and with one hand beat his breast.

"Forgive me all my sins, O God, both great and small that I have committed from the hour of my birth to this day."

He held his right glove up to God, and the angels of heaven descended to him.

Count Roland lay under a pine, his face turned to Spain, and began to mind him of many things—of the lands he had conquered by his courage, of sweet France, of his kin, of Charlemagne his lord who fostered him. He could not restrain his sighs and tears. Then he confessed his faults anew and asked forgiveness. He held up his right glove to God, and Saint Gabriel himself took it with his own hand. Then Roland's head sank on his arm, and with clasped hands he went to his end. God sent his angel Cherubin and Saint Michael. Saint Gabriel came with them. They carried the Count's soul to Paradise.

TRISTRAM AND ISEULT

OF TRISTRAM'S BIRTH

IN ARTHUR'S time, when the Knights of the Round Table were famous through all the world, there lived a King named Meliodas. He was lord of Lyonesse and was wedded to Elizabeth, sister to King Mark of Cornwall, a lady both good and fair. Elizabeth loved her lord well, and Meliodas loved her as much. So when the time came that she should bear a child, there was great joy between them.

Now upon a day, as the King was hunting in the forest and chased a hart alone, an enchantress took him prisoner. When he did not return, his Queen was almost out of her wits. She took a gentlewoman with her and ran far into the forest to seek her lord. And there in the depths of the forest she gave birth to a son with great pain and trouble.

"Ah, my little son," she said, "I see that I must die of the birth of you. I pray you, gentlewoman, when you see my lord, let him know I am full sorry to depart out of this world from him. And I charge you, beseech my lord King Meliodas to call the child Tristram, which is as much as to say, 'Sorrowful Birth.'"

With that, the Queen died. And the gentlewoman laid her under the shadow of a great tree and shielded the child as well as she could from the cold. Soon there came the barons, following after the Queen. And when they saw that she was dead, they took up her body and carried it and the child ever so tenderly home.

HOW TRISTRAM WAS MADE KNIGHT

ON THE very next day King Meliodas escaped from the prison. And the sorrow that he made for his Queen no tongue might tell. He buried her richly. Then he let the boy be christened Tristram, the Sorrowful-born child, even as the Queen had wished.

Thereafter all the King's thoughts were wrapped up in the boy. So Tristram was well nourished and taught all that a King's child should know. And when he was twelve years old, he was put in the charge of a gentleman that was well learned and taught. His name was Gouvernail. And Meliodas sent young Tristram with Gouvernail into France to learn the French tongue, and courtesy, and deeds of arms.

Seven years Tristram stayed in France. Besides the language and all things else, he learned hunting and hawking, and to play upon the harp, so that there was no harper like Tristram in any country. And when he was tall and strong and of the age of nineteen years, he returned home to Lyonesse. And his father King Meliodas had great joy of him, for the youth was loved wherever he went.

Now it happened just at this time that King Mark of Cornwall, Tristram's uncle, quarreled with the King of Ireland. For King Mark and his barons would pay no more tribute to the Irish King. And they sent back the messengers of Ireland that had come to collect the tribute with these words:

"Tell King Anguish we will pay him no tribute. And if he would have tribute of us of Cornwall, let him send a trusty knight of his land that will fight for his right. And we shall find another to defend our right."

When King Anguish heard the message, he was greatly angered. And he called to him Sir Marhaus, a knight of the Round Table and brother to the Queen of Ireland. Sir Marhaus gladly agreed to do battle for the tribute. And he arrived in Cornwall hard by the castle of Tintagil.

Then King Mark and his barons made great sorrow. For they knew no knight that dared fight against the good and noble knight Sir Marhaus. For at that time Sir Marhaus was one of the most famous and renowned knights in all the world. Every day Sir Marhaus sent word to King Mark to pay the tribute that was seven years behind, or else find a knight to fight with him. And no knight could be found.

Now word of this came to King Meliodas. And when young Tristram heard it, he was angered and ashamed that no knight in Cornwall would do battle with Sir Marhaus of Ireland.

"Alas that I am not a knight," Tristram said to his father. "If I were made knight, I would match Sir Marhaus. Sir, I pray you, give me leave to ride to King Mark. If it does not displease you, I will be made knight by him."

"Do as your courage rules," King Meliodas answered him.

The King then sent word to Sir Marhaus:
"I have found a young knight ready to do battle to the uttermost."

"It may well be," Sir Marhaus replied, "but I will fight with no knight if he be not of royal blood."

Then King Mark sent again. "A better born man than you are yourself shall fight with you. His name is Sir Tristram of Lyonesse. He is son of King Meliodas and King Mark's sister."

Sir Marhaus was glad that he should fight with such a gentleman, and it was arranged that they should meet on an island near Sir Marhaus' ships. So Tristram was put into a ship, both his horse and he. And when King Mark and his barons saw how young Sir Tristram departed to fight for the right of Cornwall, there was neither man nor woman but wept to see so young a knight risk his life for their right.

So Tristram rode to his uncle and was made a knight by him. In all haste then, King Mark had Sir Tristram horsed and armed in the best manner that might be had for gold or silver, so that he lacked nothing.

HOW SIR TRISTRAM FOUGHT SIR MARHAUS

So Sir Tristram came to the island and saw Sir Marhaus' ships at anchor on the far side. And he said to Gouvernail:

"Bring my horse to land." And when Sir Tristram was in his saddle with his shield dressed upon his shoulder, he commanded Gouvernail to go to his ship again. "Come not near this island," he said, "until you see me overcome or slain, or else that I win yonder knight." And, weeping, they departed from each other.

Now when Sir Marhaus saw Sir Tristram, he sorely pitied the youth. And he called out to him:

"Young knight, I regret your courage, for know you well, I have matched with the best knights of the world. I counsel you, return to your ship."

"Fair knight," Tristram answered him, "I may not return. It is for your sake that I was made knight. And it is your fame that gives me courage to do battle with you. For never yet have I tried myself with a good knight. And I trust I shall win honor for myself and deliver all Cornwall from tribute to Ireland forever."

"If you mean to win honor of me," Sir Marhaus replied, "you will win it if you stand me but three strokes."

With that they made ready their spears and met so fiercely that they smote each other down, horse and all. But Sir Marhaus smote Sir Tristram a great wound in the side with his spear.

Then they avoided their horses and lashed together with their swords like wild men. Thus they fought more than half a day and both were wounded, and the blood ran down freshly from them upon the ground. But Sir Tristram was fresher and better winded. And at last he smote Sir Marhaus upon the helmet such a blow that it went through the steel and through the skull, and the sword stuck fast. Sir Tristram pulled thrice at his sword before he could pull it out from Sir Marhaus' head. Then Marhaus fell down on his knees, and the edge of Tristram's sword broke off and was left in his skull. Suddenly he rose and threw his own sword and shield from him, and ran to his ships.

"Ah, Sir Knight of the Round Table," Tristram cried after him, "why do you withdraw? You shame yourself and your kin. I am but a young knight, and until now I was never tried, but I had rather be hewn in a hundred pieces than withdraw from you."

Sir Marhaus answered no word, but went his way groaning.

HOW THE QUEEN LEARNED THAT TRISTRAM SLEW HER BROTHER

THEN TRISTRAM sat him down softly on a little hill, and he bled fast. Soon Gouvernail came and put him in the ship. And when the ship came to land, the King and his barons came in procession to meet the hero. King Mark took him in his arms, and the King and Sir Dinas the Seneschal led Tristram into the castle of Tintagil. And when King Mark saw Tristram's wounds, he wept heartily, and so did all his many lords.

"So God help me," said King Mark, "I would not for all my lands have my nephew die." And he sent for all manner of physicians and surgeons, both men and women. But none could heal Tristram, for the spear which had pierced his side was poisoned.

Then came a wise lady and she said, "He will never be whole until he goes to the country that the poison came from."

So King Mark put Sir Tristram in a ship with his squire. And by fortune the knight landed in Ireland, hard by a castle where King Anguish and his Queen were. And when they heard him harping a merry lay as he sat in his bed, they sent for him.

"My name is Tramtrist," he said when they questioned him, twisting his name so that they might not know he was the slayer of Marhaus. "And I was wounded in a battle I fought for a lady."

Then the King sent for Iseult, his daughter, who was a good surgeon. She healed Tristram within a month. And he loved her greatly, for she was at that time the fairest lady in the world. And he taught her to harp, and she began to have a great fancy for him, too.

Now upon a day the Queen and Iseult made a bath for Sir Tristram. And when he was in his bath and Gouvernail attending him, the Queen saw his sword as it lay upon his bed. By misfortune she drew it out of the scabbard. And she saw that there was a great piece broken off the edge. Then she remembered the piece of sword that was found in the skull of Sir Marhaus her brother.

"Alas!" she said to Iseult, "this is the same traitor knight that slew my brother your uncle." And she ran and got the piece of sword—and it fitted.

Then she went to King Anguish and fell on her knees. "Oh, my lord," she said, "here in your house you have that traitor that slew my brother. It is Tramtrist, the same knight that my daughter healed."

"Alas!" said the King. "I am right heavy to hear it. But I charge you to let me deal with him."

Then the King went to Sir Tristram in his chamber. "Tell me," King Anguish said, "who is your father, and what is your name, and if you slew Sir Marhaus."

Tristram told him all, and when the King heard it, he said, "You did as a knight should. But I may not keep you in this country, for it will displease my barons, and my wife, and her kin."

"Sir," said Tristram, "I thank you for all that I have had with you here and the great goodness my lady your daughter showed me. And it may happen that you shall win more by my life than by my death. For it may happen that sometime in England I may do you service at some season so that you will be glad that ever you showed me your good lordship."

Then he went to Iseult and took his leave of her. "I shall be your knight all the days of my life," he said. And Sir Tristram gave her a ring and she gave him another.

After that he went to the court among all the barons. "Fair lords," he said to them, "now it is so that I must depart. If there be any man here that I have offended, let him complain before me now and I shall do what is in my power to amend it. And if there be any that will say wrong of me or shame me behind my back, say it now or never, and here is my body to make my promise good, body against body."

And there was not one that would say one word, yet there were some knights that were of the Queen's blood and some knight's that were of Sir Marhaus' blood.

HOW TRISTRAM FOUGHT A BATTLE FOR KING ANGUISH

So Tristram sailed to Cornwall and for a long time lived there in great joy. But at last envy of Tristram took hold of Mark, and gripped him.

After that, King Mark sought always to destroy Tristram. And the King thought: "If he goes again to Ireland, the Queen and her kin will surely slay him."

And so he said to Sir Tristram, "I pray you, go and ask King Anguish to give me Iseult his daughter for my wife. You have so praised her beauty and her goodness that I will wed her."

So Tristram made ready to go and took with him the best knights at court. And when he was on the broad sea, a tempest took him and his men and drove them back into the coast of England, and they arrived near Camelot and were forced to land. Then Sir Tristram set up his pavilion upon the land of Camelot.

Now it happened at this time that King Arthur had summoned King Anguish of Ireland to come to court on a certain day or lose his lands. King Anguish had come, not knowing why he was sent after. Then Sir Blamor de Ganis accused King Anguish of having slain a cousin of his. And King Anguish was abashed by the accusation because he understood full well that there was no remedy but to answer him knightly. For the custom was such in those days that if any man was accused of murder he must fight body for body or else find another knight to fight for him. And King Anguish was heavy of heart, for he knew that Sir Blamor de

Ganis was a noble knight. And the judges had told the King that he must give answer by the third day.

Now Gouvernail learned that King Anguish was put in great distress, and why, and told it to Tristram.

"These be the best tidings that ever came to me this seven year," Sir Tristram said, "for now the King of Ireland has need of my help, and to win his love I will take the battle upon me. Therefore, go you to King Anguish and say I would do him service."

King Anguish came with all speed when he heard Tristram was there, and they clasped arms around each other.

"My gracious lord," the knight said then, "I promised you to do my service if ever it lay in my power."

"Never had I so great need of a knight's help," King Anguish said.

And Tristram said, "For the good lordship you showed me in Ireland, and for my lady your daughter's sake, I will take the battle for you upon these conditions. One is that you shall swear to me you are in the right and never consented to the knight's death. Then, when I have done this battle, if God give me grace that I speed well, you shall give me a reward, whatever reasonable thing I ask for."

"Truly," said the King, "I am guiltless of this murder, and you shall have whatsoever you will ask."

So Tristram took the field with Sir Blamor de Ganis, and they made ready their spears and came together like thunder. And Sir Tristram smote down Sir Blamor and his horse to the earth. Then Sir Blamor pulled out his sword and bade Sir Tristram to alight.

"For though a horse has failed me, the earth will not fail me," said he.

Sir Tristram alit then, and they lashed together strongly, racing and tracing, foining and dashing many sad strokes, so that the kings and knights who looked on wondered that they had breath to stand on their feet. And all the place was bloody that they fought in. But at last Sir Tristram smote Sir

Blamor such a blow that he fell down upon his side, and Sir Tristram stood and looked at him.

When Sir Blamor could speak, he said, "Sir Tristram de Lyonesse, I require you, as you are a noble knight and the best knight that ever I found, that you will slay me out. For I had rather die with honor than live in shame. I will never say, 'I yield me.'"

Tristram knew not what to do, for Sir Blamor de Ganis was of Lancelot's blood, and for Lancelot's sake Sir Tristram would not slay him. And yet he had no choice but to slay him if Sir Blamor did not beg for mercy. So Sir Tristram went to the kings that were judges and kneeled down before them and beseeched them to take the matter in their hands, for he would not slay this noble knight nor shame him.

"And as for the King for whom I fight, I shall require him to have mercy upon this good knight," Tristram said.

So the kings called the King of Ireland and found him good and responsive. And then by their advice, Sir Tristram and Sir Bleoberis, Sir Blamor's brother, took up the knight, and the brothers made peace with King Anguish.

And for that gentle battle all the kin of Sir Lancelot loved Tristram forever.

HOW TRISTRAM AND ISEULT
DRANK A LOVE DRINK

THEN King Anguish and Sir Tristram sailed into Ireland. And when the Queen heard what Tristram had done, she made much of him. But the joy that Iseult made of Sir Tristram no tongue might tell, for of earthly men she loved him most.

"But why have you not asked your boon?" King Anguish said to Tristram one day. "For I promised you should have it without fail."

"Sir," said Tristram, "now it is time. And this is all that I desire: that you will give me Iseult your daughter, not for myself, but for my uncle, King Mark, that he shall have her to wife, for so I have promised him."

"Alas," said the King, "I would rather you wed her yourself."

"Sir, if I did, then I would be shamed for ever in this world and false to my promise."

"You shall have her," King Anguish said, "to do with her what it pleases you. I would rather you wed her yourself. But you may give her to King Mark, your uncle, if that is your choice though it sorely grieves me."

So Iseult the Beautiful was made ready to go with Sir Tristram, and Dame Bragwaine went with her for her chief gentlewoman. And the Queen gave Dame Bragwaine and Gouvernail a flask in which was a love drink. And she said:

"On the wedding day give this drink to King Mark. Let him drink to Iseult, and then they will love each other all the days of their life."

And so Sir Tristram took to the sea with Iseult. And when they were in the cabin, it happened that they were thirsty, and they saw the little flask of gold and drank freely to each other. Then they laughed and made good cheer and they thought that no drink they had ever drunk to each other was so sweet nor so good. And when the drink was in their bodies, they loved each other so well that their love never departed, not one day of all the days of their life.

HOW SIR TRISTRAM WAS DRIVEN INTO A CHAPEL

KING MARK and Iseult were richly wed.
But ever the young Queen and Tristram sought to be together. And Sir
Andred, his cousin, watched Tristram night
and day to slander him.

Now one day Sir Tristram stood talking
with Iseult at a window, and Sir Andred
saw them and told it to the King. Then King
Mark took a sword in his hand and came to
Tristram and called him false traitor and
would have struck him. But Sir Tristram
ran under his sword and took it from him.

"Where are my knights and my men?"
the King cried. "I charge you, slay this
traitor!"

But not one would move. So King Mark
bided his time.

And another time Sir Andred found Tristram with Iseult. Sir Andred had twelve
knights with him then, but Tristram was
unarmed. So they set on him and bound
him and led him to a chapel which stood
upon the sea rocks. And when Tristram saw
that there was no remedy but he must die,

he said, "Fair lords, remember what I have done for the country of Cornwall, and in what danger I have been for the good of you all. When I fought for the tribute of Cornwall with Sir Marhaus the good knight, I was promised to be better rewarded. Therefore, as you be good gentle knights, see me not thus shamefully die."

"Fie upon you, false traitor that you are!" said Sir Andred. "For all your boast, you shall die this day."

"O Andred, Andred," Tristram said, "you should be my kinsman, and you are full unfriendly to me. If there were no more here but you and I, you would not put me to death, but you would spare me."

"No!" said Andred. And he drew his sword and would have slain him.

Then Tristram looked upon both his hands that were fast bound to two knights. Suddenly he pulled them both to him and wrenched his hands free. Then he leaped to his cousin Andred and wrested his sword out of his hands and smote Sir Andred so that he fell to the earth. And Sir Tristram fought until he had killed ten knights.

But meantime there was great cry outside, and people drew fast to Andred, more than a hundred. When Sir Tristram saw this, he broke the bars of a window and leaped out and fell upon the crags of the sea. And Tristram was saved at that time.

HOW ISEULT SOUGHT TO SLAY HERSELF

THEN Gouvernail came and found his master on the rocks and pulled him up. But for a long time after he was rescued, Tristram endured great pain. For many months he was like one who had lost his mind. He ran naked in the wilderness and broke down trees and boughs, and harped and wept, and would never come into any town or village. He fell in with herdsmen and shepherds, and they would give him of their meat and drink. But if he did anything that displeased them, they beat him with rods. And they clipped his hair with shears and made him like a fool.

Then Sir Andred brought to King Mark's court a tale that Tristram was dead. This he

did because he wished to have King Mark give him Sir Tristram's lands and make him King of Lyonesse.

Now when Queen Iseult heard the tidings, she made such sorrow that she was almost out of her mind. And one day she sought to slay herself. She got a sword and thrust the sword through a plum tree up to the hilt so that it stuck fast and stood breast high. Then she kneeled down to pray.

"Sweet Lord Jesu," she said, "have mercy upon me, for I may not live after the death of Sir Tristram de Lyonesse. He was my first love, and he shall be the last."

She would have run upon the sword but that King Mark came into the garden and saw her as she knelt. He took her up in his arms and bore her to a strong tower, and kept here there, and watched her surely. And Iseult lay long sick after that.

HOW TRISTRAM WAS BANISHED OUT OF CORNWALL

THEN a knight bore to King Mark a tale of how there was a wild madman by the well that was in the forest. So he went with his knights and his hunters to hunt in that forest. And there he found lying a naked man, and a sword by him.

"Take him up fairly," King Mark said to his knights, "and bring him to my castle."

So they cast mantles upon Sir Tristram and led him to Tintagil. There they bathed him and cared for him till they had brought him to his senses. But all this while there was no creature that knew what man he was.

Now Queen Iseult heard how the King had brought a wild man to the court. And one day she said to Dame Bragwaine, "Come

on with me, for we will go see this man that my lord brought from the forest."

Tristram was in the garden, lying in the sun. And Iseult looked on her love and did not know him, so changed was he. But Tristram knew her well enough, and he turned away his face and wept.

Now the Queen always had by her a little dog that had once been Tristram's and that he had given her when Iseult first came to Cornwall. And this little dog leaped upon Sir Tristram and licked his cheeks and his ears, and then whined and smelled at his

feet and hands, and knew him very well.

"Ah, my lady," said Dame Bragwaine, "alas, alas! I see it is mine own lord, Sir Tristram!"

Thereupon Iseult fell down in a swoon and so lay a great while. And when she could speak, she said, "My lord Sir Tristram, blessed be God you are alive. And now I am sure you will be discovered, for this little dog will never leave you. Therefore, mine own lord, grant King Mark his will, and then go you to the court of King Arthur, for there you are beloved. And I shall send letters to you when I may, and at all times I will be at your command to live as poor a life as ever did queen or lady."

Then came King Mark and with him Sir Andred. And the dog bayed at them.

"Sir," said Andred, "this is Sir Tristram, I see by the dog."

And the King said to Tristram, "Tell me your faith and what you are and what is your name."

"Truly," said Tristram, "my name is Sir Tristram de Lyonesse. Now do with me what you like."

"Ah," said King Mark, "I am sorry you have recovered."

Then he called his barons to judge Tristram to death. But many of them would not assent. "Banish him out of the country for ten years," they said.

Thereupon Sir Tristram took his oath upon a book before the King and his barons that he would stay out of Cornwall for ten years. And he made ready immediately to go to King Arthur's court.

Some who were his friends and some who were his foes put Tristram on his ship. And he spoke bitter words to them.

"Greet King Mark and all my enemies," he said. "Say to them I will come again when I may. And well am I rewarded for the fighting with Sir Marhaus and delivering all this country from tribute. And well am I rewarded for fetching Queen Iseult out of Ireland!"

Forthwith he set sail. And Iseult thought: "He will come back for me. I care not if I live as poor as ever lady did, so long as I may be with Tristram."

HOW KING MARK AND TRISTRAM WERE BROUGHT TO ACCORD

Now Sir Tristram won great honor in King Arthur's court. In all the jousts and tournaments he sped so well that no knight but Lancelot surpassed him. And King Arthur was angered that so good a knight had been banished out of Cornwall. So on a day when King Mark had come to Camelot, Arthur said to him:

"I pray you, give me a gift that I shall ask of you."

"Sir," said King Mark, "I promise you whatsoever you desire if it be in my power."

"Gramercy," said King Arthur. "This I will ask you: that you will take Sir Tristram with you into Cornwall, and let him see his friends, and there cherish him for my sake."

"Sire," said King Mark, "I promise you by the faith of my body, and by the faith I owe to God and to you, I shall honor him for your sake."

"Swear that upon a book before me," said Arthur.

King Mark swore on a Bible before King Arthur and all his knights. And then King Mark and Sir Tristram gripped each other hard by the hands.

But when Sir Tristram made ready to ride with King Mark, many in King Arthur's court were angry. For most of the Round Table feared that King Mark would slay Sir Tristram. And especially Sir Lancelot was angered out of measure.

"Alas," he said to King Arthur, "what have you done? You will lose the man of most honor that ever came into your court."

"It was Tristram's own desire," King Arthur answered, "and therefore I could not do otherwise. I made them at accord."

"Accord!" Sir Lancelot cried. "Fie upon that accord, for you shall hear that he will slay Sir Tristram or put him in prison, for he is the most cowardly and villainous king that is now living."

Therefore Lancelot went to King Mark and said to him, "Beware, I counsel you, of treason. For if you do treason to that knight, I swear I shall slay you with my own hands."

"Sir Lancelot," said the King, "you have said overmuch to me. I have sworn before King Arthur and all his knights and it would shame me to break my promise."

"You speak well," said Sir Lancelot, "but you are called so false and full of treason that no man may believe you. I know well you came into this country for no other cause but to slay Sir Tristram."

Then Tristram, all trusting, went with King Mark. And all this was so that he might see Iseult, for without the sight of her Tristram could not live.

HOW KING MARK REVENGED HIMSELF ON TRISTRAM

So Tristram came again unto Iseult. And of the joy that was between them, there is no tongue can tell it, nor heart think it, nor pen write it. But Sir Lancelot knew well how it would be with King Mark. It was not long before the King broke his oath and put Tristram in prison.

Then Iseult made as great sorrow as ever lady made. And Tristram sent a letter to her, saying, "If it please you, make ready a ship for you and me and we will go to King Arthur's realm."

"Be of good comfort," Iseult answered him. "I will make the ship ready and all things to the purpose."

And she went to Sir Dinas the Seneschal and told him the treason of the King.

"I pray you," she said, "take King Mark

and put him in prison until Sir Tristram and I have departed out of Cornwall."

And Sir Dinas promised her. For there were knights at King Mark's court that honored Tristram because he surpassed all others but Lancelot. Sir Dinas took counsel with them, and they put King Mark in prison.

Then Iseult and Tristram took to the sea. And Lancelot brought them to his own castle, Joyous Gard.

But King Mark had his revenge on the lovers at last. For again Tristram put trust in the King's word and returned to Cornwall and gave Iseult back to the King. Then, on a day when the knight sat harping before his lady, King Mark ran his sword through Tristram from behind. And Iseult died swooning on the corpse.

Thus was the work of the drink accomplished that Tristram and Iseult drank.

RUSTEM

RUSTEM KILLS THE WHITE ELEPHANT

ONE NIGHT sudden uproar sounded in the house of Zal, the Pehliva of Zaboulistan. On all sides voices shouted: "The Pehliva's white elephant has broken his chain in fury!"

Rustem awoke. He sprang out of bed and ran towards the door. There was such a roaring outside that the walls of the house shook to their foundations.

"Let me pass into the court!" the ten-year-old boy cried.

But the guards barred the way. "How can we answer for it before the Pehliva your father if you run into danger?" they said.

Rustem forced a passage with his mighty arms and with his strong fists broke down the iron barriers and strong bolts of the door.

There was the elephant, raging in its madness, and there stood the warriors, huddled in a corner of the wall. Rustem was ashamed for them in his soul. He seized a club and ran towards the huge beast with a loud cry. The eyes of the elephant flashed fire. He raised his trunk to strike the boy down. Then Rustem beat the creature upon the head with his club and smote him so that he died.

Afterwards Rustem went back to bed and slept soundly till morning. But news of the boy's prowess spread throughout the house of Zal, and far into the land, and all rejoiced because a new hero had risen in Iran.

ND SOHRAB

RAKUSH THE LIGHTNING FOOTED

Nᴏᴛ long after this, the Shah of Iran died. Across the border in Turan, King Afrasiyab learned that the throne was empty.

"This is my moment," he thought. And raising an army, he marched into the land to seize the seat of power.

"Help us!" the people cried to Zal as they had many times before.

And the Pehliva said to them, "Ever have I looked after you. But old age is upon me now. I charge you, therefore, look to Rustem my son to deliver you. Though he is young, he shall be backed by the wise counsels of his father."

Then Zal called Rustem before him.

"O my son," he said, "your lips still smell of milk, and pleasure should be all your desire. But the days are grave, and Iran looks to you in its danger."

"You know that I care not for pleasure," Rustem answered. "Give me, O my father, a strong steed, and let me go out to meet the hosts of Afrasiyab."

When Zal heard these words, his heart laughed within him. "Let the herds of Zaboulistan and also those of Cabul be brought before my son," he commanded.

So it was done. And as the horses passed before Rustem, he laid his hand on the back of each to see if the steed could bear his weight. But every horse of Zaboulistan shuddered as it bent beneath his grasp, and all sank upon their haunches.

Then the herds of Cabul were driven up, and Rustem saw in their midst a mare mighty and strong. And after her came a colt like the mother, with the chest and shoulders of a lion, and in color like rose leaves scattered on a saffron ground.

"There is my steed," thought Rustem. "It is as strong as an elephant."

So he made a running knot in his cord and threw it about the colt and drew it towards him, though the mother defended it mightily.

The keeper ran up when he saw what Rustem did.

"O youth," he cried, "do not take the horse of another!"

"To whom then does it belong?" Rustem asked. "I see no mark on its flanks."

"We do not know its master," the keeper answered, "but there are rumors about it throughout the land, and men call it the Rakush of Rustem. I warn you, the mother will not permit you to ride it. It has been ready for the saddle these three years, but she would let none mount it."

When Rustem heard this, he swung himself on the colt in one bound. Then the mare ran at him to pull him down, but hearing his voice, she stopped. And the rose-colored steed bore Rustem away like the wind.

Back he came over the plains. "Tell me, I pray you," he said to the keeper, "what is the price of this dragon?"

"If you are Rustem," the keeper replied, "mount him and save Iran from its sorrows. The price of Rakush is the land of Iran."

So Rustem rode away on Rakush, whose name means *lightning,* and came to Zal, and they made ready to stand against Afrasiyab. And it came to pass that Rustem broke the power of the host of Afrasiyab and set Kai Kobad on the throne of Iran. And Turan made peace with Iran.

TAHMINEH WOOS RUSTEM

For many years Kai Kobad ruled over Iran in great glory, so that no king could be likened to him. Then he died and his son Kai Kaous seated himself on the throne. Kai Kaous was not wise like his father, but puffed up with idle pride. Every wind bore him away. He entered into one folly after another. And each time he got himself in trouble, he sent for Rustem. Time and again Rustem came to his rescue, and all knew that if not for the son of Zal, Afrasiyab would be sitting on the throne of Iran. Then at last Kai Kaous learned his lesson and steadied himself and ruled gloriously.

Now it happened in these latter years of his reign that Rustem awoke one morning and was filled with sadness.

"I will go out to the chase," he said to himself, "and drive away this heaviness."

So he saddled Rakush and filled his quiver with arrows and rode out into the wilderness near Turan in the direction of the city of Samengan. At his approach a herd of wild asses started up. For a long time he made sport among them. Then, weary of the chase, he killed one and roasted it, and having eaten, lay down to sleep. Rakush meantime cropped the pasture grass.

Now while Rustem slept, seven knights of Turan passed by. They saw the beautiful rose-colored horse grazing, and they said, "Truly that would be a good capture for us." And they readied their cords to snare Rakush.

But the horse pawed the ground and fell upon them. He bit off one man's head, another he struck down with his hoofs. But in the end they snared Rakush and took him swiftly away.

Rustem was beside himself when he awoke and saw that Rakush was gone.

"How can I stand against the Turks without him, and how shall I cross the desert alone?" he thought. He saw the signs of struggle and the trail leading towards the city, and he knew that Rakush had been stolen by men of Samengan.

So he followed the trail. And when those within the city saw Rustem coming on foot, the King and the nobles went out to meet the hero.

"My horse was stolen as I slept," he told them angrily, "and his tracks have led me to your gates. If Rakush is not restored to me, many will die."

"Peace, peace!" the King of Samengan said

121

to him. "None of my people shall do you wrong. Surely Rakush cannot be hid."

So Rustem went in, and they feasted him and surrounded him with every honor. And when night came, he was led to a couch perfumed with musk and roses. And he lay down and slept.

Now very early in the morning he heard his chamber door open. A slave bearing a lamp came in, and behind her came a woman whose beauty was veiled. They came near his bed and stood there.

"Who are you and what do you desire?" Rustem asked.

Then the veiled woman drew her veil aside, and Rustem saw that her beauty was like the moon.

"I am Tahmineh, the daughter of the King of Samengan," she said. "None of the princes of this land is worthy of me and none has seen me unveiled. But I have heard of your deeds and your great prowess. My eyes have yearned to look on your face. And now that God has brought you within the gates of my father, I am come to tell you that I am yours if you will hear me, and if not, I will wed no other. And if you will listen to me, I will lead before you Rakush your steed, and I will place Samengan under your feet."

Rustem had filled his eyes with her beauty as she spoke, and now when she mentioned Rakush, it was not difficult for him to make up his mind. That very morning he sent to the King and asked the hand of Tahmineh his daughter.

The King was overjoyed when he knew that Rustem desired his daughter. And all in the house and the city of the King rejoiced that Tahmineh had been given to the hero Rustem, son of Zal.

Now when Rustem and Tahmineh were alone, he took from his arm an onyx which the whole world knew and gave it to her.

"Cherish this jewel," he said. "If you give birth to a daughter, fasten it in her hair. And if you bring forth a son, fasten it on his arm that he may wear it like his father."

The day passed quickly, and toward evening the King came to them with tidings that Rakush was found. Then Rustem knew the time had come for him to depart. He took Tahmineh into his arms and bathed her face with his tears and kissed her hair. Then he flung himself on Rakush and rode away from Tahmineh.

SOHRAB, WHOSE LIPS WERE FILLED WITH SMILES

Now when nine months had passed, Tahmineh bore a son in the likeness of his father. And all men called him Sohrab because his lips were filled with smiles. The babe grew from day to day so that it was marvelous to see. At one month he was like a child of twelve. At five years he was skilled in all the arts of war. At ten none could stand against him in games of strength.

Then he came to his mother and said, "Teach me my race and my family, so that I shall know what to say when men ask me the name of my father."

Tahmineh smiled joyously and she said, "You are the son of Rustem and are descended from Zal, the son of Saum. And since God made the world there has been in it none like Rustem your father."

Then she showed him a letter which she had received from Rustem, and gave him the gold and jewels the hero had sent when the boy was born.

And she said, "Cherish these gifts. But close your lips concerning that which I have told you. For Turan groans under the hand of Afrasiyab, and he is an enemy of your father's. If Afrasiyab should learn about you, he would destroy you. Moreover, I would not have your father learn that you have become such a mountain of valor. For if he knew it, perhaps he would demand you of me, and then your mother's heart never would be whole again."

"Nothing can be hidden forever," Sohrab replied. "And since my birth is so noble, I will go into Iran with an army of brave Turks, and will cast Kai Kaous from the throne and set my father there instead. Then together we will conquer the land of Turan, and I shall slay Afrasiyab and mount the throne in his stead. And you shall be called Queen of Iran. Oh, I pant for the battlefield! But I need a horse to bear me, for I cannot go before my enemies on foot."

Tahmineh saw little wisdom in this plan of her tall, ten-year-old son, but she rejoiced at his courage. So she ordered the herds of horses to be led out before Sohrab. And he tested their strength as his father had once done. But no horse could satisfy him. Then a man brought before him a foal sprung from Rakush. Sohrab tested it and found it strong and sprang on its back. "Now that I have this horse," he cried, "I can face my enemies!" And he made ready for war.

The warriors flocked around Sohrab, and the King of Samengan opened his treasure house to his grandson, for he was filled with delight at this boy.

Now Afrasiyab heard of the preparations against Iran, and once more he thought, "The hour has come." So he called to him his chieftain Human and said to him:

"It is known to me that Sohrab of Samengan is Rustem's son. Let it be kept from Rustem who it is that goes out against Iran. Then perhaps the young lion will slay his father. Without Rustem, Iran will fall into our hands. Then we will overcome Sohrab also, and the whole world will be ours."

Afrasiyab told Human to go with an army to Sohrab, bearing gifts. And he wrote to Sohrab, saying: "If Iran is overcome, the world will know peace. For I will place the crown of Iran on your head. And Turan, Iran, and Samengan will be as one land."

Sohrab was too young to understand the guile of Afrasiyab. He rejoiced at the help sent to him, and now he believed that none could stand against him. So the cymbals clashed and the army went forth into Iran and laid all waste before them. And they came to the White Castle, the great fortress in which Iran put its trust.

GURDAFRID THE WARRIOR MAID

UJIR was the guardian of this fortress, a brave man and loyal. When he saw from afar the cloud of armed men, he came out alone to meet them. And Sohrab taunted him for his rashness. Hujir taunted him in return. Then Sohrab challenged him to come near and fight with him. And Sohrab overcame Hujir as though he were an infant, and bound him, and sent him to Human.

Now Hujir's daughter, the beautiful Gurdafrid, was in the castle, and she was a warlike maid, skilled in battle and accustomed to the saddle. When she heard the wailing around her because Hujir her father had been overcome, she was ashamed. She clad herself in her coat of mail, hid her hair under a helmet, mounted a battle steed, and rode out before the walls. And she defied the warriors to come forth to single combat.

"I will accept your challenge," Sohrab cried, and he rode toward her.

Then the maid rained arrows at him like hail. Sohrab was unable to defend himself, and covering his head with his shield, he spurred

his horse at her. She dropped her bow and thrust at Sohrab with her lance so that she all but unseated him.

Fury took hold of Sohrab then. He ran at her and caught her by the waist and threw her on the ground. But before he could

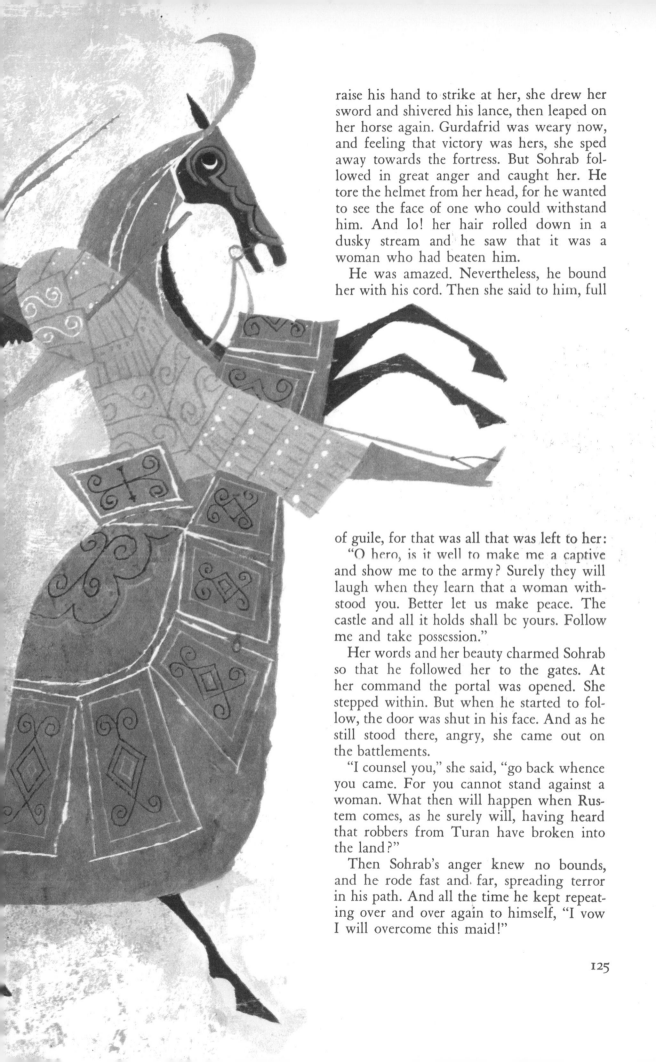

raise his hand to strike at her, she drew her sword and shivered his lance, then leaped on her horse again. Gurdafrid was weary now, and feeling that victory was hers, she sped away towards the fortress. But Sohrab followed in great anger and caught her. He tore the helmet from her head, for he wanted to see the face of one who could withstand him. And lo! her hair rolled down in a dusky stream and he saw that it was a woman who had beaten him.

He was amazed. Nevertheless, he bound her with his cord. Then she said to him, full of guile, for that was all that was left to her:

"O hero, is it well to make me a captive and show me to the army? Surely they will laugh when they learn that a woman withstood you. Better let us make peace. The castle and all it holds shall be yours. Follow me and take possession."

Her words and her beauty charmed Sohrab so that he followed her to the gates. At her command the portal was opened. She stepped within. But when he started to follow, the door was shut in his face. And as he still stood there, angry, she came out on the battlements.

"I counsel you," she said, "go back whence you came. For you cannot stand against a woman. What then will happen when Rustem comes, as he surely will, having heard that robbers from Turan have broken into the land?"

Then Sohrab's anger knew no bounds, and he rode fast and far, spreading terror in his path. And all the time he kept repeating over and over again to himself, "I vow I will overcome this maid!"

RUSTEM COMES

Next morning Sohrab made ready to fall upon the castle. But when he came near, he saw that it was empty. The doors stood open. Vainly he searched for Gurdafrid—in the darkness all had fled by an underground passage.

Now a message had been sent from the White Castle to Kai Kaous, Shah of Iran.

And when the Shah read it, he was greatly afraid. He called his nobles about and said:

"An army has come out of Turan against us. At its head rides a chief that is a child in years but a lion in strength and stature. Who shall stand against this Turk?"

"We can look only to Rustem," his nobles all agreed.

So Kai Kaous sent an urgent letter to the Pehliva and told him all, adding: "Stay not to speak the word that hangs on your lips. If you have roses in your hands, do not stop to smell them. But haste to help us in our need."

Rustem read the letter through. Then he said to the messenger:

"I cannot believe that a warrior of renown should rise up among the Turks. I myself have a son in Samengan, but he is yet a child and his mother writes me that he delights in the sports of his age. Though he will likely be a hero among men, his time has not yet come to lead an army."

So Rustem made ready and went to the Shah. Together they led out the legions of Iran and came to the plains where stood the fortress of Hujir. And they set up their pavilions a little distance away.

Now Sohrab's watchman saw them from the battlements as they came, and he set up a great cry. But when Sohrab saw the enemy, he rejoiced and asked his warriors to a banquet of wine.

"Be of good cheer," he said, "for I see no hero in their ranks who can stand against me. Let us feast until it is time to meet the foe in battle."

Night came. Then Rustem said to the Shah:

"Let me go beyond the camp that I might see what manner of man this stripling is."

So Rustem disguised himself as a Turk and entered the castle in secret. And he saw Sohrab tall as a cypress, with arms strong and sinewy. Brave warriors were about him. They drank the wine which slaves poured before them, and were glad.

Now Tahmineh had sent Zindeh her brother forth with her son, because Zindeh alone of all the army of Samengan knew Rustem and could point him out to Sohrab. For she feared that harm might befall him

126

if the heroes should meet in battle. Zindeh was drinking there with Sohrab. After a while, Zindeh changed his seat and came near the spot where Rustem stood watching. Zindeh saw him in hiding and said:

"Who are you? Come out that I may see your face in the moonlight."

Before he could say anything more, Rustem struck him down dead.

When Zindeh did not return to the feast, Sohrab became alarmed and sent men to look for him. And they found him lying in his blood. But Rustem they did not find, for he had gone quickly back to his own camp.

THE LOYALTY OF HUJIR

NEXT morning, Sohrab put on his armor and went out on the heights from which he could look down on the camp of the Iranians. And he took Hujir with him.

Sohrab said, "If you tell me the truth, I will loosen your bonds and give you treasures. But if you speak falsely, you shall remain in chains."

With this, Sohrab pointed to a pavilion of gold brocade adorned with leopard skins. Before its doors stood a hundred elephants. Within could be seen a throne of turquoise and over it floated a violet standard with a moon and sun worked in its center.

"Tell me whose pavilion that is?" Sohrab asked Hujir.

"It belongs to the Shah of Iran," Hujir replied.

"And whose is that black one over which floats a standard whereon is worked an elephant?"

"It is the tent of Tus, the son of Nuder."

"And to whom belongs the tent of many colors draped with green? I see upon its throne a Pehliva nobler than all his fellows, and beside him stands a steed tall as he."

Now this was Rustem's pavilion. But when Sohrab asked about it, Hujir thought: "If I tell this lion the signs whereby he may know Rustem, surely he will seek to destroy him." And he said to Sohrab, "That is some ally of Kai Kaous from far Cathay. His name is not known to me."

Then Sohrab was downcast that he could not discover Rustem. It seemed to him that he saw in this Pehliva the marks by which his mother had said he would know his father, but he could not believe his eyes against the words of Hujir. He went on to ask about the other pavilions, but again and again he asked about the green-roofed tent. And Hujir replied that he did not know whose it was.

"Where then is Rustem?" Sohrab asked.

"He tarries in Zaboulistan," Hujir replied, "for it is the feast of roses."

But this Sohrab refused to believe. He knew that Kai Kaous would not go forth to battle without Rustem.

"If you do not show me the tent of Rustem," he cried, "I will strike your head from off your shoulders! Choose, therefore! The truth or your life!"

Hujir neither trembled nor grew pale. He thought, "Five score men cannot withstand Rustem when he is roused to battle fury. Yet it might come about that if they meet, this stripling will subdue the Pehliva. And what does my life matter against the good of Iran?"

So he said, "Why do you seek to know Rustem? Surely you will know him in battle, and he will strike you down. I will not show him to you."

At these words, Sohrab's blood boiled. He raised his sword and smote, and made an end of Hujir. Then, leaping on his steed of battle, he rode to the camp of the enemy. He broke down the barriers with his spear and called out in a voice of thunder:

"Come out from your pavilion of gold, Kai Kaous, and do battle with me! For I swear that the blood of Zindeh my uncle, slain treacherously by Iranian hands, shall be avenged!"

Confusion spread through the camp when the Iranians saw Sohrab and heard his bold words. None of those who stood about Kai Kaous dared to accept his challenge. They said that of all men only Rustem could defend them from the enemy.

So Tus sped to the courts of Rustem. Then, while some of the nobles buckled on the hero's armor and threw his leopard-skin about him, others saddled Rakush. And they pushed Rustem forth and called after him:

"Hurry, for this is no ordinary combat that awaits you!"

SOHRAB AND RUSTEM MEET

Now there was a place between the two camps that none might pass, and where all could view the combat. So when Rustem came before Sohrab, he said:

"Let us step forth from the lines of the armies."

Sohrab agreed, and they took up their positions. But when Sohrab would have fallen upon him, the soul of Rustem melted with pity for this boy, and he desired to save him. So he said:

"O youth, the air is warm and soft, but the earth is cold. I would not take your life. Yet if we fight, you will surely fall by my hands, for none have withstood my power. Stop, and leave the ranks of Turan. Come over to us, for Iran has need of brave heroes like you."

It seemed to Sohrab that his heart went out of him when he heard that voice. He looked at Rustem and said:

"O hero, I beseech that you reply truly to my question. Tell me your name, that my heart may rejoice at your words. For it seems to me that you are Rustem, the son of Zal."

But Rustem answered, "You are wrong. I am not Rustem. Rustem is a Pehliva, but I, I am a slave and own neither a crown nor a throne." This he said only to discourage Sohrab. For he thought, "Let him believe

128

when he sees my prowess that there is still greater might hidden in the camp of his enemy."

But when he heard Rustem's words, Sohrab was sad, because his hopes were shattered. He made ready for combat, and they came together and fought until their spears were shivered and their swords were like saws. And when all their weapons were bent, they took their clubs and fought with them until they were broken. Then they wrestled with each other with their hands until the sweat ran down their bodies. Their throats were parched, their bodies weary, but neither had the victory. So they stopped a while to rest. And Rustem thought that in all his days he had not battled against such a hero.

After a time they began again, and fought with arrows. Then Rustem tried to hurl Sohrab from his steed, but he could no more do it than he could move a mountain. So they took to clubs once more. And Sohrab smote Rustem so that he reeled and bit his lips in agony.

Then they parted, and Rustem fell on the men of Turan, while Sohrab raged along the lines of Iran. And Rustem was sad in his soul and turned to his camp with sorrow. But when he saw men and horses fall under Sohrab's hands, he cried:

"O youth, come forth yet again to single combat with me!"

"The day is far gone," Sohrab replied. "Let us therefore rest until tomorrow."

Rustem agreed to this, and each went his own way.

Then Sohrab sought out Human. "My mind is filled with thoughts of this aged man with whom I fought," Sohrab said. "My heart goes out to him, and I wonder if he is Rustem, my father. I beg you, tell me how this may be."

But Human remembered Afrasiyab's words that he should lead Sohrab into destruction, and he answered.

"Often have I looked upon the face of Rustem in battle. This man in no way resembles him, nor is his manner of fighting the same."

THE SECOND BATTLE

Now when the day began to lighten the sky, Rustem and Sohrab once more strode forth to the place between the armies. Sohrab bore in his hands a mighty club. But Human's words had not wholly satisfied him, and the hero's heart still yearned toward his foe. With a mouth full of smiles he addressed Rustem:

"Why have you prepared your heart for battle? Rather let us take off our armor and seat ourselves in friendship, and drink wine, and my heart shall speak to you of love. I ask you yet again to tell me your name. Hide it no longer, for I see that you are of noble race. And it seems to me that you are mighty Rustem, the Lord of Zaboulistan, the son of Zal."

But Rustem answered "O hero of tender age, we have not come forth to talk, but to fight. I am an old man, and you are young, but we are girded for battle, and the Master of the World shall decide between us."

Then Sohrab sighed, for his heart was heavy. But, like Rustem, he bound his steed, and they fell upon each other. Throughout the camps the crash of their warfare was heard like thunder. And they fought from morning to the setting of the sun. Then at last Sohrab seized Rustem by the girdle and threw him down upon the ground and kneeled upon him and drew forth his sword to cut off his head. And Rustem knew that only guile could save him, so he said:

"O young man, you do not know the customs of the combat! According to the laws of honor, he who overthrows a brave man for the first time should not destroy him. Only on the second fall is it given to him to kill his enemy."

Sohrab listened to Rustem's words of craft. He let Rustem go, and they fought no more that day.

But when Human heard what had happened, he said to Sohrab, "Alas, young man, you fell into a trap, for this is not the custom among the brave. And now, perhaps, you will yet fall under the hands of this warrior."

Sohrab was ashamed. But he said, "He will not stand a third time against my youthful strength."

FATHER AND SON

RUSTEM meantime was praying to God in his distress: "Grant me such strength, O Ormuzd, that the victory must be mine!"

And Ormuzd heard him and gave him such strength that the rock on which he stood gave way under his feet because it had not the power to bear him.

Now came the time of the combat. Rustem turned to the meeting place. His heart was full of cares and his face of fears, but Sohrab came forth like a giant refreshed. He ran at Rustem like a mad elephant, and cried with a voice of thunder:

"O you who fled from battle, why have you come out once more against me? This time your words of guile will not help you!"

And Rustem, looking at him, knew fear. But he closed on Sohrab with all his new-found strength and shook him terribly. And though Sohrab returned his attacks, the hour of his overthrow had come. For Rustem took him by the girdle and hurled him to the earth and broke his back like a reed. Then he drew forth his sword to cut the head from the body.

Sohrab knew it was the end. He gave a great sigh and said "What has come about is my own fault, and now my youth will be a cause of laughter among the people. But I did not come out for empty glory. I came to seek my father, for my mother had told me by what tokens I should know him, and I perish for longing after him. It has not been given me to look upon his face. Yet I say to you, if you should become a fish that swims in the depths of the ocean, if you should change into a star that is hidden in the farthest heaven, my father would draw you forth and avenge my death upon you. For my father is Rustem the Pehliva, and it shall be told to him that Sohrab his son perished in the search."

When Rustem heard these words, his sword fell from his hand. The earth became dark before his eyes, and he sank down lifeless beside his son. But after a time he came to himself once more. Then he cried out to Sohrab:

"Have you a token of Rustem that I may know that the words which you speak are true? For I am Rustem the unhappy, and may my name be struck forever from the lists of men!"

Sohrab heard, and his misery was dark and boundless.

"If you are indeed my father," he cried, "then you have stained your sword in the lifeblood of your son! And you did it out of your own stubbornness. For I tried to turn you to love, and I begged you to tell me your name. But I appealed to your heart in vain, and now the time for meeting is gone. Yet open my armor, and look at the jewel on my arm. For it is an onyx given me by my father as a token by which he should know me."

Rustem did as Sohrab bade him. And when he saw the onyx, he tore his clothes in distress. Tears ran from his eyes and he roared aloud in his sorrow.

But Sohrab said:

"It is in vain. There is no remedy. Do not weep, for doubtless it was written that our meeting should end so."

"I CAME LIKE THE THUNDER AND I VANISH LIKE THE WIND"

Now when the sun had set and Rustem had not returned to camp, the nobles of Iran went out to seek him. They had gone but a little way when they came upon Rakush. And when they saw that he was alone, they began to wail, for they thought that surely Rustem had perished. So they went back and told Kai Kaous.

"Let Tus go forth and see if this indeed be so," the Shah said. "And if Rustem be truly fallen, let the drums call men to battle that we may avenge him upon this Turk."

Sohrab saw the nobles far off as they came out to seek Rustem. "I entreat you, do me an act of love," he said to his father. "Do not let the Shah fall upon the men of Turan. For they came not in enmity to him, but to do my desire. As for me, I came like the thunder and I vanish like the wind. But perhaps it is given to us to meet again not on the bloody battlefield, but above."

So Rustem left his son and went to the men of Iran. And when they saw that he was alive, they set up a great shout. But then they saw that his clothes were torn and his face sad, and they asked him what had come to pass. And he told them. Then he bade one among them to go to Human in the camp of Turan with this message:

"The sword of vengeance must slumber in the scabbard. You are now leader of the host. Return, therefore, from whence you came. As for me, I will fight no more. Neither will I speak to you again, for you hid from my son the tokens of his father and led him into this pit."

Then Rustem went back to his son, and the nobles went with him. And Rustem would have made an end of his own life, but the nobles stayed his hand. And when Sohrab had departed from this world, Rustem set up such a sorrowful wailing as the earth had never before heard:

"I that am old have killed my son. I that am strong have uprooted this mighty boy. I have torn the heart of my child, I have laid low the head of a Pehliva."

Then he made a great fire and flung into it his tent of many colors, and his trappings, his saddle, and his leopard-skin, his armor well tried in battle, and all that belonged to his throne. And he stood by and looked on to see his pride laid in the dust. And he tore his flesh and cried aloud:

"My heart is sick unto death!"

Then he commanded that Sohrab be wrapped in rich brocades of gold. And afterwards, when the Turanians had left the land, he made ready to return to Zaboulistan. All the nobles marched before the bier, their heads covered with ashes, and their garments torn. And the drums of the war-elephants were shattered, and the cymbals broken, and the tails of the horses were shorn to the root.

And when he had come home to Zaboulistan, Rustem built for Sohrab a tomb in the shape of a horse's hoof and laid him in a chamber of gold perfumed with ambergris. And when it was done, the house of Rustem became like a grave. No joy would enter the heart of Rustem, and it was long before he held his head high.

Meanwhile the news spread even to Turan, and there, too, all men mourned for Sohrab. The King of Samengan tore his clothes. But Tahmineh was beside herself with grief.

She heaped black earth upon her head, and tore her hair, and wrung her hands, and rolled on the ground in her agony. Then she ordered that his steed be brought to her. And she stroked him and poured tears upon his hoofs, and she pressed his head to her breast. Then with Sohrab's sword she cut off the tail of the steed, and set fire to the house of Sohrab, and gave his gold and jewels to the poor. And when a year had thus rolled over her bitterness, the breath departed from her body, and her spirit went forth after Sohrab her beloved son.

133

SIGURD OF THE VOLSUNGS

TWO CAPTIVES

ALF, son of King Hjalprek of Denmark, came sailing along the shore with his army. And a strange sight met his eyes. The earth was strewn with a great number of men and horses slain in some fierce battle. Yet no living soul was there to strip the dead, and but for the carrion crows that flapped and settled and rose again, no thing in all that place stirred. Then off in the distance Alf saw two women hurrying into a dense wood.

"Let us land!" he said to the Vikings. And he gave commands for the women to be found and brought to him. They came, not unwilling. And Alf saw that one was tall and fair and carried herself proudly, but was clad in mean garments, while the other, who looked less noble, wore the garments of a queen.

"Who are you?" Alf asked them.

And she who was clad like a queen spoke for both. She told how King Sigmund of

Hunland had met his doom here, and many another valiant man with him, and that King Lyngvi had done this deed.

"Know you where the royal treasure is?" Alf asked.

"Indeed we know," the woman answered, and showed him where she and the other woman had hidden it. And it was great wealth, so that Alf and his men had never before seen so much gathered together in one place—gold cups and flagons, and rings, and bracelets, and armbands, and golden chains to wear about the neck. The men bore all the treasure to King Alf's ships, where lay much more spoil besides. For Alf was the boldest of men. And the two women followed him into the high-prowed ships, and they went over the water to Denmark.

HJORDIS TELLS THE TRUTH

Now when Alf had been home but a short time, the Queen, his mother, said to him—for she was a woman wise in the ways of the world and had had much experience of men and things:

"My son, why has the fair dame fewer rings and meaner garments? It seems to me that she whom you have valued less must be the nobler."

And Alf answered, "I have suspected the same thing, mother. It seems to me that the fair woman who calls herself Hjordis does not have the nature of a bondwoman. For when we first met, she knew how to give greeting to noblemen. I shall make a test of them and we shall see what we shall see."

So one day at a feast Alf said to her who wore the queen's garments, "Tell me. How do you know when the dawn is near if you are sleeping and cannot see the moon or any of the stars?"

And she answered, "This is how. In my youth I was accustomed always to have a mighty drink at dawn before I went out to tend the cattle. And I still awake at the same time."

The King smiled. "That is a strange thing for a king's daughter to do," he said.

Then he sought out Hjordis and asked her the same, and she replied, "My father gave me a small gold ring of such nature that it grows chill on my finger towards dawn. That is my sign that the night is passing into day."

Then the King said, "There must have been plenty of gold in your land if the maid-servants wore it! Now you have concealed from me long enough that you are a king's daughter. If you had told me, I should have treated you as if we were both the children of a king. But I shall deal with you even better now, for you shall be my wife."

Then she told him the truth about her lot.

"I am King Eylimi's daughter," she said, "and was wife to King Sigmund who met his death on that field where you found me. When I saw your painted ships coming to the shore, I was afraid. So I changed garments with my maid-servant that she might seem more worthy in your eyes and I might escape attention. And now, since you would make me your wife, I wish you to know that King Sigmund is dear to me still and that I carry his child under my heart."

And King Alf answered her with all courtesy, saying, "I will wait and give you dowry when your child is born."

So Hjordis abode there in the greatest honor, and to all she seemed the noblest of women and truly a queen.

SIGURD AND REGIN

Now HJORDIS gave birth to a boy, and he was brought before King Hjalprek, Alf's father. The old King rejoiced when he saw the bright eyes of the newborn child.

"None will ever be his equal!" he said. "Let him be called Sigurd if his mother is willing."

So the child was sprinkled with water and given the name Sigurd. And he was reared under the eyes of King Hjalprek with great love. For never did child equal him in growth or deeds. And as he advanced in years, he was ever in the lead among his fellows because of his strength and skill and boldness. He knew well how to wield a sword and cast a spear; how to throw a shaft and hold a shield; how to span a bow and ride a steed. And all the little children loved him and yearned to be like him.

Sigurd was reared in King Hjalprek's hall, and Regin, who had the knowledge of many things, was set to teach him. He taught Sigurd all sorts of skills—chess and runes and many tongues of men and other things fitting for kings' children to know. Also Regin was skilled in many ways, but he was an evil man who ever tried to sow suspicion in the boy's heart and to break him away from those that loved him.

"Why do you trust them so?" he would say to Sigurd. But the boy had a loving, open

heart into which evil could not find its way.

One day Regin came to speak with Sigurd and said, "It is strange that you should be the Kings' stable boy or run on their errands."

Sigurd tossed the brown curls that hung to his shoulders. "It is not so," he replied, "for I take counsel with them in everything, and all that I desire is granted me."

Then Regin said, sneering, "Ask the King to give you a horse."

"He will give it to me, I know. You shall see. It will be at once as I will."

The King's eyes lit up when the boy came to him. "What would you have of us?" he asked.

Sigurd answered, "I would have a horse for my pleasure."

"Choose yourself the horse you would have. Take any one of ours," King Hjalprek answered him.

Then Sigurd went back to Regin. "I go to choose a horse," he said. "Give me your counsel."

"That is not hard," Regin said. "Let us drive the herd deep into the river."

So they did. And as soon as the horses could not feel bottom under their feet, they all tried to climb back on shore. Only one swam across. That one Sigurd took. It was gray in color, young and large and fair. When he caught it, it stood quite still and let him mount him, though none had ever done so before. And when it felt the prod of the boy's heels, it went off like the wind, yet so smoothly that Sigurd clung to the mane and did not fall off.

"Regin!" Sigurd shouted. "This is my steed."

And when he had galloped back, the horse stood by him as though it knew that he was its master. The boy stroked its silken neck and said, "I shall call him Grani!" And Sigurd set about getting a saddle and other gear for his horse, and King Hjalprek gave him golden spurs.

But still Regin tried to sow discontent. And he said to Sigurd, "The King gives you too little. It grieves me that you go about like a village churl. Your father King Sigmund had great wealth. And where is it now?"

"The Kings hold it for me," Sigurd said. "It is fitting that they should do so until it falls to me, for they can watch over it better than I."

Regin smiled his evil smile and shrugged his shoulders as if he doubted. Then he said, "It is no matter. For I can tell you, Sigurd, where much gold is to be had. It would be a deed of great honor to seek it. And if you can take it, you will have great glory."

Sigurd did not like the glint in Regin's eye, yet he could not but ask, "Where is this gold? And who guards it?"

"There is a dragon called Fafnir who lies not far away on Gnitahead," Regin said. "If you go there, you will see more riches gathered in one place than you have ever beheld. Never would you need more—not even if you should become the oldest and most famed of kings."

"I know about that dragon," Sigurd said. "And I have heard it said that none dares to go against him because he is so great and so cruel."

"It is not so," said Regin. "He is reported to be much greater than he really is. Your ancestors the Volsungs would not have thought him too great. But though you are a Volsung, you do not have their spirit!"

"It may be so," Sigurd answered and his blue eyes blazed. "Yet there is no need to taunt me who am only a boy and little beyond childhood. But why do you urge this so strongly on me?"

"I have reasons," Regin said. He would not give them and only looked out craftily from under his lids. After a time, he repeated, "There will be much glory for you, Sigurd, if you can kill Fafnir."

But Sigurd knew that Regin sought Fafnir's death for some reason of his own. Still Sigurd was all aflame with desire to kill the dragon. And he said:

"Make me a sword by your cunning, Regin, so that none shall be its like and I may do great deeds with it. Do this if you desire that I slay that great dragon."

"I will do it!" Regin said. "And you will be able to kill Fafnir with that sword."

the blade was hammered out, he plunged it into water to temper it, then gave it to Sigurd.

Sigurd raised the blade aloft and smote the anvil with it. And the sword shattered.

"Such is your smithying, Regin!" Sigurd cried and cast the blade aside. "Make me one better than that!"

"It is a hard thing to be your smith," Regin said. But he made another sword and brought it to him.

Sigurd looked at it and felt the sharpness of the edge with his finger.

Regin said, "This one must surely be pleasing to you."

Sigurd went to the anvil and tested the sword as he had done the other. And it broke even as the first.

"Would you betray me?" Sigurd cried. "I will have no sword that will not cleave the anvil."

After that he went to his mother where she sat in her hall embroidering fair stuffs with gold.

"Is it true, mother, as I have heard," he said, "that King Sigmund gave the sword Gram to you in two parts?"

"It is true," Hjordis said, and her heart leaped up to see the eagerness in her tall son's eyes. For she knew that now the time had come to give Sigurd the broken sword King Sigmund had given her when he lay dying on the battlefield and she held his head in her arms.

"Give them to me," Sigurd said. "I would have them."

So Hjordis went to her carven chest and took from it two pieces of a sword. She held them close to her breast, there where she knelt. Then she held them out to Sigurd.

"I have kept your father's sword for you as he bade me," she said. "King Sigmund won great fame with it so that his name was renowned to the ends of the world. You are likely to win great glory with that sword, Sigurd, for never was there its equal."

Sigurd scarcely heard his mother's words, so taken up was he with looking at the sword. He turned the pieces over and over in his hands and read the runes upon the hilt. For Regin had instructed him and he had the knowledge of runes. Then he laid the

THE BROKEN SWORD

REGIN had such skill in working iron that there was no craftsman to compare with him. He went into the smithy. The apprentices blew up the forge and watched him beat the hot iron. When

two pieces on a table and fitted them together. And they stood there—Sigurd and his mother Hjordis—looking at the sword. And it seemed to Sigurd that fire played all around the edge.

"Do you know, mother," Sigurd said at last, "who made this mighty sword?"

Hjordis shook her head: "I know only what your father told me of it and what the bards sang of it in your father's hall. But who made the sword I do not know, my son."

"It must be that it was his father's before him," Sigurd said.

"Nay," Hjordis answered. "King Volsung never had it." She laid her arm on Sigurd's shoulder and drew him down beside her on the bench. But his eyes never left the great sword as she went on speaking, and ever and ever again his hand stole out and lovingly clasped the well-wrought hilt.

SIGNY'S MARRIAGE FEAST

Now THIS is the tale Hjordis told her son Sigurd when she gave him the sword Gram. And the words that came to her lips were those she had often heard when snow lay in heaps about King Sigmund's hall and the wild wind blew and tales were told of the deeds of stalwart men:

"Many fires were kindled down the length of King Volsung's great hall and the tables groaned under the weight of good cheer. For it was the marriage night of Signy, King Volsung's daughter. Nine sons had he and this one fair daughter.

"King Siggeir had journeyed from Gautland and asked her in marriage. King Volsung had received his wooing favorably, as did his sons, too, for King Siggeir was rich and had many followers. As for Signy herself, she was unwilling. But she let her father rule her in this matter as in all else that concerned her. And now on the appointed day the guests of both Volsung and Siggeir were come together to feast and celebrate the marriage.

"Right merrily the flames leaped, lighting up the tables heaped with roast meats and fine wheaten bread and flagons of wine and mead. Yet the eye of every guest as he entered fell first on the great oak tree that stood in the midst of the hall. For never was a hall built like this, around a tree so that the limbs of the tree with their fair leaves upon them went out over the roof and the trunk stood within.

"Now when the feasting was done and men sat about the fire in the evening, a stranger entered the hall. He wore a spotted cape and a hood. He was barefoot, and his linen breeches were bound at the knee, while on his head he wore a wide hat. He was hoary and aged and had but one eye. And in his hand he carried a sword. He walked straight up to the great oak, raised the sword aloft, and thrust it into the trunk so that it sank in to the very hilt.

" 'He who can draw this sword from the tree,' he said, 'shall have it of me as a gift. And he will find, in truth, that he never bore better sword in his hand than this one.'

"Then the old man went out of the hall, and none knew who he was or where he afterwards went.

"The guests arose. One by one they tried to draw forth the sword, the noblest going first. But none could make it so much as quiver a little when he laid hands on it. And now came Sigmund, son of King Volsung. He was Signy's twin brother, ever foremost among the King's sons. And lo! it was as though the sword lay loose there for him. He put both hands on the hilt and the sword came forth easily.

"Each man thought the weapon so good that he had never seen its like before. And the bridegroom said, 'I will give you thrice its weight in gold.'

"But Sigmund answered him, 'You could have taken that sword just as I did if it had befitted you to bear it. But now you shall never have it—even though you should offer me all the gold that you have.'

"King Siggeir was angry at these words. However, he was crafty by nature and he

acted as though he had not heard what Sigmund said. But the next day—though it was not men's custom to go from a marriage feast after one night of celebration only—he made ready to depart.

"Then Signy said to her father, 'I have no wish to depart with Siggeir! And I feel that great sorrow will come to us if we do not quickly undo this marriage.'

"'You should not say that, daughter,' King Volsung answered her. 'We must hold our side of the pact.'

"So Signy entered the great painted ship, though her thoughts did not smile towards Siggeir and she did not wish to depart.

"Now King Siggeir had invited King Volsung to visit him after a space of three months, together with all his sons and as many followers as he wished. But Siggeir did this only to revenge himself for the scornful

words that had been spoken concerning the sword. And when at the appointed time the guests came ashore in Gautland, Siggeir fell upon them with ax and sword and spear. The Volsungs struck back, but the strength against them was more than they could withstand. King Volsung was slain and all his men with him. Only his nine sons were left alive, and they were put in bonds and led away.

"Then Signy begged the King to come to her. And she said to him:

"'I know that it would avail me little to beg for my brothers' lives. But do not have them killed at once. For the eye takes delight in what it still sees.'

"'You are mad and of small wit,' Siggeir answered her, 'to beg more torment for your brothers than being slain. But it shall be as you wish. They shall see one another die.'

"So he had a great stock made and put on the feet of the nine brothers, and they were set down in a wood. All day they sat there until the night. And at midnight a fierce she-wolf came and bit one of them to death. And after that she ate him up entire and went away.

"Now early in the morning Signy sent the man she trusted most to see what had befallen. And when she learned that one of her brothers was dead, it grieved her to think that all might share the same fate and she might not be able to help them. Each morning she sent the man to bring her news, and ever it was the same—the she-wolf came and devoured one of the brothers. When only

Sigmund was left, Signy said to her faithful vassal:

"'Take honey and smear my brother's face with it, and put some of it in his mouth.'

"So the man did it. And that night when the she-wolf came, she smelled the honey and licked Sigmund's face. After that she thrust her tongue into his mouth. He bit hard on the tongue of the wolf. She started to pull away then. The she-wolf pulled so fiercely that with her feet she broke the stock apart. And Sigmund was free.

"He lived in the forest. There he built himself a house underground. And Signy gave him what he needed. But King Siggeir thought that all the Volsungs were dead.

"Now Signy brooded ever on revenge, and when her eldest son was ten years old, she sent him to Sigmund. He put a bag of meal into the boy's hands.

"'Bake bread for us,' he said, 'for I must go and get firewood.'

"But the boy did nothing. And when Sigmund returned and asked him why, he said: 'I dared not because there was something alive in the meal.'

"'This boy is not brave enough to be of use to me,' Sigmund thought. And he sent the child back to his mother.

"When Signy's second son was ten, she sent him out, too. But it went just as before. Then she sent her third son, Sinfjotli. And Sigmund tested him as he had done the others, saying, 'Knead this meal while I go out to seek firewood.'

"When he came back, Sinfjotli had finished the baking.

"'Did you find anything in the meal?' he asked the boy.

"'There was something alive in it when I first took to kneading it,' Sinfjotli replied. 'But I kneaded in whatever was there.'

"Then Sigmund laughed aloud. 'You shall not eat of that bread,' he said, 'for you have kneaded into it a most venomous snake.' And to himself he said, 'I have a true Volsung now to help me avenge my kin. But he is yet too young. I will first accustom him to hardship.'

"So Sigmund kept Sinfjotli by his side. And the years sped.

"Then one day Sigmund and Sinfjotli went to King Siggeir's dwelling and hid in the room which was before the great hall, among the beer casks that were there.

"Signy's two youngest children were playing with a golden toy. They cast it on the floor of the hall and ran after it. But all of a sudden a golden ring rolled from the toy and went into the room where Sigmund and Sinfjotli were hid. One of the boys ran after it. He saw the two men with helmets on, sped back to the hall, and told his father what he had seen. Then the King suspected treason against him. The two men defended themselves well, but in the end they were borne down and bound and fettered.

"The King thought a long time about what long-drawn-out death he might give them. When morning came, he had a great mound built of turf and stones. In the middle of it he had a stone slab set on edge, dividing the mound in two. Then he set Sigmund on one side and Sinfjotli on the other that they might not be together, yet could hear each other speak.

"Now when the thralls were covering the mound over with turf, Signy came by with some meat wrapped in straw and threw it down to Sinfjotli. And she said to the thralls, 'Say nothing about it to the King.'

"Then came the night. Sinfjotli unwrapped the straw and behold! a sword was thrust into the meat. He felt of the hilt and knew that it was Sigmund's sword.

"'The Queen has sent us your sword,' he said joyfully. Then he thrust the sword point over the slab and pulled hard so that it bit into the rock. And Sigmund took hold of the sword-point, and they sawed the rock between them and sawed through both iron and stone until they were out of the mound.

"Then they went to the King's hall where the men were lying all asleep. They carried wood into it and set it on fire. And when the thick smoke rolled through the hall and the flames roared and leaped to the roof, the men sprang up and ran here and there all choked and blinded with the smoke and could not find the door.

"The King awoke in the midst of it. 'Who made this fire?' he cried out.

"And Sigmund answered him, 'Here am I with my sister's son Sinfjotli, and we intend

you to know that not all the Volsungs are dead as you desired!'

"Now Signy stood by the door. And Sigmund bade her come with him and he would make up to her for all her woe. But she answered him, saying, 'I worked so mightily to bring about this revenge that I do not want to live on hereafter. Gladly will I die now with King Siggeir, though against my will I married him.'

"And she kissed her brother and went in and died there in the fire with Siggeir and all his men.

"Then Sigmund gathered ships and men and went back to his own country and cast out the man who had taken it after King Volsung. And he ruled the realm and grew to be a rich king, wise and daring and famed to the far corners of the world."

FORGED ANEW

SIGURD sat silent a long time after Hjordis had done speaking. For the woes his father had endured weighed on him so that it seemed to him his heart would burst. He knew that many a day would pass before he would be able to cast off the spell of his mother's speaking. He longed to go out, to feel the sun and fresh air, to hear speech of common things, and know surely that the grim happenings his mother had told were in the past. But he sat still for a long while.

"Take up your sword now," Hjordis said after a time.

Sigurd rose and wrapped the two pieces in the yellowed linen. Then he kissed his mother. And when he tasted the salt tears on her face, a great love welled up in him for her and for the father he had never seen.

"I will go at once to Regin," he said.

And Regin marveled greatly when he beheld the blade—never had he seen such a fine sword.

"It was my father King Sigmund's sword and now it is mine," Sigurd said proudly. "Gram is its name. Now make it whole for me, Regin, and if it breaks like the others, then you are no maker of swords."

But Gram did not break. Next day when Sigurd struck the anvil, it was the anvil that broke. It split to the base, but the sword did not even chip.

Then Sigurd's face beamed with gladness. "It is a fine sword, Regin, a marvelous sword!" he said.

And Regin answered, "There can be none better. Many a sword have I wrought, but never one like this that hews hardest iron as if it were flesh."

"I shall test it yet again," Sigurd said. "My sword shall be sharp even as it is strong!"

Beside the open smithy door an apprentice sat and polished a shield. Sigurd said to him, "Give me a tuft of your wool, Ragnar."

And when the other gave it to him, wondering, Sigurd went to the stream that flowed by the smithy and cast the tuft in against the current. Then he held the sword in the water, and when the wool drifted down against the blade, lo! the tuft was cut in two.

"You are a sword for great deeds!" Sigurd said, holding the blade high. He strode away rejoicing, thinking to show Gram to his mother the first of all.

THE DEATH OF SINFJOTLI

HJORDIS sat plaiting her hair when she heard the door open. She turned and saw Sigurd standing upright, resting both hands on the hilt of his sword. And a little cry escaped her. It seemed to her that this tall son of hers had grown years older overnight.

"Sigurd!" she said. "Or is it Sigmund? For you are so alike that it startles me. Your father's hair was white and his face lined. But just so his broad shoulders sloped, and so he held his proud head, and so he stood leaning on his sword!"

She went to him and laid her hands on his breast and looked deep into his eyes. And suddenly she gave a sob and hid her face.

Then Sigurd laid the sword down and held her to him, saying, "I did not come to make you weep, mother. This is a time for gladness. For I am come to my strength now and have my sword and shall do great deeds with it even as my father did. Though it cannot be that I should equal him," he added.

She took her hands from her face. "My tears are not for you, Sigurd," she said, "but for him. A twelve-month only I was wedded to your father, and to Alf have been a true wife since. But I grieve yet that I was not by your father's side when his blood was hot and his face smooth and he went back to Hunland to take the Volsung realm. For there was no woman then to comfort him for his great woes. Borghild was not a woman for that."

Sigurd made Hjordis sit and knelt down on the floor by her.

"Mother," he said softly, "tell me your thoughts. So will you get ease and I understanding. I would know all that concerns my father."

Hjordis sat silent, her clasped hands stone-cold in her lap and her eyes set on something afar. At last she spoke:

"Your father, Sigurd, had a wife before me," she said. "Borghild was her name."

She paused, thinking Sigurd would ask some question, but he did not. So she went on with her tale.

"Borghild hated Sinfjotli. And your father loved him as none other, for they two had endured much together. Borghild would have had Sinfjotli leave the realm, for he had slain her brother in a quarrel. But your father would not have him depart. And when she saw she could not have her way,

she made ready a great funeral feast for her brother. And she herself carried drink about to the men.

"She came to Sinfjotli with a great horn and said: 'Drink!'

"He took the great horn, looked into it and said, 'The drink is bewitched.'

"'Give it to me!' your father cried and drank it down.

"Then the queen came a second time with the horn. 'Drink now!' said she.

"'The drink is full of deceit,' Sinfjotli said, taking the horn.

"'Give it to me!' your father said and drank it down, too.

"The third time the queen came, saying, 'Drink if you have the Volsungs' courage!'

"Sinfjotli took the horn and said, 'There is poison in the drink.'

"'Drink it through your beard!' your father said to him.

"By this, Sigurd, he meant that Sinfjotli should only pretend to drink and should spill the liquor on the ground. But Sinfjotli mistook his meaning. He emptied the horn into his mouth—and fell dead.

"Then your father was near to death with grief. He could not be comforted. And he sent his queen away from him, and soon afterwards Borghild died."

SIGMUND'S LAST BATTLE

"It was after that, Sigurd," Hjordis continued, "that your father wooed me. He came with many ships over the water. And when we learned that he came not to make war, my father, King Eylimi, prepared a great feast for him.

"But there came to that feast also King Lyngvi, son of Hunding, who likewise sought to wed me. Then my father was dismayed. For both could not gain their errand, and he feared the one who did not succeed would make war against us. He came to me and said:

"'Hjordis, you are a wise woman, and I have said that you shall choose your own husband. Choose now between the two kings.'

"And I said to him, 'Father, this matter is difficult to decide. But I choose the king who is more famed, and that is King Sigmund, though he is far older.'

"So I was given to him, and Lyngvi went away. All could see that he was angry. And I thought, 'He is planning evil.' But the feast went on, and every day there was greater and richer entertainment than the day before. After that your father took me home to Hunland. And King Eylimi went with us, for he feared the warfare of Lyngvi.

"And he had good reason to fear. A year had not quite passed when King Lyngvi and his brothers came to Hunland with a great army, determined to destroy the pride of the Volsungs. And they sent word to your father from their ships: 'We have no wish to take you by surprise. For we are sure you will not flee from us.'

"So your father gathered together an army and he said to me, 'Hjordis, I have a foreboding of evil. I would not have you fall into Lyngvi's hands. Nor would I that he got the wealth I have won with this my sword. So take the treasure and take a maid-servant with you and go out into the woods. And if the battle goes against us, you will know what to do.'

"He kissed me then and went forth. And I took the treasure and one maid-servant and we followed the men. And we went up on a height and stood at the edge of the wood, where we could look down and see all that passed.

"Your father set up his banners and let blow the trumpets. Then the Vikings leaped

ashore from their ships, and it seemed to me they were without number. When the battle began, I looked neither to the right nor left, but kept my eyes on your father. He was old, Sigurd, but his fighting was keen. Again and again he charged the ranks of the foe. Many a spear was thrown at him and many an arrow shot, yet he got no wound. And I lost count of those who fell before him.

"But when the battle had gone on for a time, I saw a man coming towards him, and he was none of Lyngvi's men nor ours. For, instead of a helmet and shirt of mail, he wore a wide hat and a cape. In his hand he carried a spear and lifted it up before your father. And as the King still hewed fiercely with his sword, it struck against the spear and so split apart.

"After that, many of your father's men fell. He fought on, but at last he, too, fell and my father, King Eylimi, with him.

"And when King Lyngvi knew that he had the victory, he left the field. I saw him go the way to your father's hall, and no doubt he thought to find me there and take me away. Afterwards they all went into their ships and sailed. Then I ran to the battlefield. And there, amidst the hacked-off limbs and bloody bodies of the slain, I found your father where he lay and took his head in my arms.

" 'Sigmund!' I said. 'Can you be healed?'

"And he answered, 'I will not have myself

healed, for all my good fortune has left me.'

"He gave me the shattered sword. 'Keep it,' he said. 'From it a good one may be made. With it our son will do great deeds which shall never grow old, for his name shall live on while the world endures.'

"After that he spoke no more. And I sat over him until he died. . . ."

Dusk had come on while Hjordis told her tale, and now Sigurd could no longer clearly see her face. His own was very pale. He rose and took his sword and came and stood before her. And when she lifted up her eyes to him, he said:

"Be comforted, mother. Think not that my father will be unavenged. Gram and I will let King Lyngvi know well that all the Volsungs are not dead!"

UNDER THE OAK

SIGURD went from his mother and flung himself down under a great oak tree. For his thoughts were not on bread and meat, but on the things which he had just heard.

Often had he climbed this mighty oak. Often had it been his stronghold, defended with wooden sword against the foe, his merry playmates. He knew its every limb, knew every foothold and just where one must pass from branch to branch to gain the very top. But now in the dusk it was not this oak he saw but that other which had stood in his grandfather King Volsung's hall and spread its limbs and fair leaves over the roof.

A thousand thoughts went through his mind as he lay there with the rustle above and around him. Who was the one-eyed stranger who had thrust the sword into the trunk so that none might draw it forth save Sigmund his father? Who was the man in wide hat and cape that came on the battlefield and held out the spear on which the mighty blade had shattered? Odin it must have been. For good or for ill the god had watched over his father. And how would it be with Sigmund's son now that the sword was his? Would the god so watch over him?

The sound of footsteps broke in on Sigurd's thoughts. Regin had come to look for him.

"What are you doing here?" Regin said. "And why did you not come to supper? King Hjalprek looked at your empty seat and questioned me, and I knew not what answer to make."

Sigurd sprang up. He did not speak, but only grasped his sword in both hands and leaned on it and looked at Regin.

"A noble sight you are," Regin said scornfully. "But swords are made to use, not to lean upon. And now that I have made you one to your heart's desire, you must slay Fafnir as you promised."

Sigurd replied, "I shall do it indeed. But not before I have avenged King Sigmund and my other kinsmen who fell in battle."

And he strode away while Regin looked after him, gaping.

Suddenly Sigurd felt hunger. He did not go to King Hjalprek's hall, for he wished none to question him. He went to the kitchens where the cooks plied him with the best they had. Sigurd was ever a favorite with the cooks as he was everywhere and with all.

SIGURD AVENGES HIS FATHER

NEXT MORNING Sigurd sought out King Hjalprek and King Alf. He stood before them with his sword, and they marveled where he had got such a one. Yet more they wondered at the new manhood that had come over the youth and at the light that shone in his eyes—as though he were filled with the will to do great deeds.

Sigurd greeted them according to the custom. Then he said, "For some time have I been here. And my debt to you is great for your love and the great honor done me, who was born of a captive woman. But now I wish to leave this land and seek the sons of Hunding. I wish them to know that the Volsungs are not all dead. For this I crave your help."

King Hjalprek answered, "For the love we have given you and the honor we have done you, you owe us no thanks, Sigurd. They have been paid for a thousand times by the joy we have had in you. As for the help you crave, you shall have all you ask."

Then King Alf spoke. "It is right, Sigurd, and your high duty to avenge your father. The gods will strengthen your hand, for you go to fight in a just cause."

So a great army was assembled, and all things carefully prepared, both ships and arms. And when Sigurd's men took their places in the vessels and the sun sparkled on their shields and shirts of mail, it seemed to all that this journey would be more splendid than any before. Sigurd himself steered the ship which was greatest and noblest. But the sails of all of them were splendid to see.

Now a favoring wind followed them all the way, so that in a short time they came to land in the kingdom of Hunding's sons. There they poured out fire and steel. They slew men and burnt dwellings and laid waste the land as they went on. And the foe fled before them to King Lyngvi, saying: "The Volsungs are not all dead. It is Sigurd, Sigmund's son, that leads the army now."

Then King Lyngvi sent out a summons to war throughout all his realm and called to him every man who would serve him. And he met Sigurd in battle. Many an arrow could be seen flying and many a spear. The axes were red with blood. Shields were cloven and shirts of mail slit, and many a man fell to the earth.

When the battle had gone on for some time, Sigurd advanced, carrying the sword Gram. He hewed down both horses and

men, and charged through the ranks with his arms bloody to the shoulders. Men fled wherever he came, and all thought that they had never seen his like before.

The battle lasted a long time, with fierce fighting and great slaughter of men. Then all the sons of Hunding came together, and in a body they attacked Sigurd, who was in the front ranks among his men. Sigurd struck at King Lyngvi and clove his helmet and head and his armored body. Then he turned on the brothers, who pressed at him from all sides. And he slew them all and the greater part of their men.

And now, having won a fair victory and fame, Sigurd went home to Denmark, his ships heaped high with the booty he had taken in this war. Great was the rejoicing at his homecoming. Throughout all the kingdom feasts were held in his honor. In King Hjalprek's hall Hjordis herself went about bearing drink to the men. And the gladness in her eyes was more to Sigurd than the praise of the Kings.

Afterwards Regin came to speak to Sigurd.

"Now you will be wishing to slay Fafnir as you promised," he said, "for you have now avenged your father and your other kinsmen."

Sigurd answered, "True. Now I will keep my promise to strike down the dragon."

THE SLAYING OF FAFNIR

ONE DAY Sigurd and Regin rode up on the heath to Gnitahead. And they saw there the track by which the dragon Fafnir was accustomed to creep when he went down to the water.

"You told me, Regin," Sigurd said, "that Fafnir is not so great as he is said to be. But to me his tracks seem exceedingly great."

"No matter," Regin said. "The way to fight him is simple. Make yourself a pit in his track and get in it. Then when the dragon crawls to the water, strike upward at his heart and give him his death. And for this you will win great fame."

"What if the dragon's blood hinders me and I drown?" Sigurd said.

Regin stamped his foot in rage. "None will give you counsel if you are afraid," he said. "You have not your kinsmen's courage!" And he turned his horse and rode away, for he was greatly afraid himself.

Sigurd got down from Grani and led him away into the bushes. Then he came again and dug a pit directly in the dragon's track. He covered it over with heath grass, and got in the pit and waited.

Then came the dragon creeping to the water, and the earth quaked so that all the land quivered. The whole way before him Fafnir blew forth poison. But Sigurd had no fear or terror. When the dragon crawled over the pit, Sigurd plunged the sword in under the left shoulder, as deep as the hilt. Then he leaped out of the ditch and snatched the sword again. And when the dragon felt itself wounded to death, it struck about with head and tail so that all things before it burst. And it roared:

"Who are you? And who urged you on to this deed?"

"I am called Sigurd, Sigmund's son," answered Sigurd. "My bold spirit urged me on to this."

"I counsel you," Fafnir said, "take your horse and ride away swiftly, for it often happens that he who received a death wound avenges himself for it."

"Such is your counsel," Sigurd said, "but I shall do otherwise. For I shall ride to your lair and take your great store of gold. Lie there, Fafnir, in your death struggle till Hell takes you!"

And Fafnir said, "You have not deceived me. I know well that it is Regin who has wrought my death. And it gladdens me that he is working for your death also." And with these words Fafnir died.

After that Regin came riding back.

"Hail, my lord!" he cried when he saw Fafnir dead. He got off his horse and bowed before Sigurd. "You have won a great victory, for no man before was bold enough to stand in Fafnir's path. And the fame of this deed will live on while the world remains."

Sigurd took his sword Gram and dried it on the grass. "You went far away while I did this deed," he said. "In your fright you knew not which was heaven and which was earth." And he laughed right merrily.

"Have your fill of laughing," Regin said hotly. "Fafnir would be yet alive if you had not had the aid of this sword which I made for you with my hands."

"A stout heart is better than a sharp sword," Sigurd replied.

Regin said no more, but went up to Fafnir and touched him with the tip of his shoe. Then he drew his sword and cut out the dragon's heart and brought it to Sigurd on the tip of the blade.

"Grant me a prayer that will cost you little," said he. "Take the heart of Fafnir and roast it and give it to me to eat."

Sigurd saw the craft in Regin's face and heard it in his voice, and he remembered Fafnir's dying words. Yet he saw no harm in doing what Regin asked of him. So he took the heart and set it on a spit. Then he built a fire and roasted the heart of Fafnir, and when it frothed over, he tested it with his finger to see if it was done. His finger was scorched, so he put it in his mouth. And lo! when the blood of the dragon came upon his tongue, he understood the speech of birds. And he heard some nuthatches chattering in the brushwood beside him.

Said one, "There sits Sigurd roasting the heart of Fafnir. He should eat it himself, for then he would be wiser than all other men."

Another said, "There lies Regin, who would deceive him who trusts in him."

And a third said, "It would be well if Sigurd should slay him, and if he rode after that to Fafnir's lair and took all the gold that is in it. And next he should ride up on Hindarfell where Brynhild sleeps. He would learn great lore from her."

And a fourth said, "He is not so wise as I thought if he spares Regin, who would be his death."

Sigurd looked at Regin where he lay in the grass, watching him craftily, and he thought, "A wolf is to be found where a wolf's ears are. I have had warning enough. Now I shall do as the birds advise, for it is clear that the fates do not intend that Regin shall be my death."

And he drew his sword and struck off Regin's head.

Then he quickly mounted Grani and rode along Fafnir's tracks as far as his dwelling. It was dug into the ground, and the iron doors were open. Sigurd went in. There he found a great store of gold. It seemed to him that two or three horses could scarcely carry it. But he took all of it and carried it out to Grani in two great chests. Then he pulled Grani by the reins, but the steed would not move. Sigurd understood what Grani desired. He leaped on its back and pricked the horse with his spurs. And Grani galloped forward as if he were not loaded at all.

BRYNHILD

SIGURD rode on a long way, turning southwards to Hindarfell as the little birds had advised. And suddenly he saw far off upon a cliff a great brightness, as if fire burned there and leaped to the very heavens. He wondered much what it might be. So he rode quickly and went up the cliff, and when he came near he saw that in truth there was a ring of fire.

"Leap!" he said to Grani.

The brave steed answered to the spur and plunged through the flames. Then Sigurd saw before him a rampart of shields and a banner above them. Dismounting, he went into the enclosure of shields. And behold! a man lay there on a couch, asleep in full armor.

"I will see what man it is that sleeps in the midst of fire," Sigurd thought, and coming close, he took the helmet from the man's head. Then he saw that it was a woman, for two great yellow plaits were twisted about her head.

"Awake!" he cried. "You have been asleep too long!"

The woman stirred and opened her eyes. And when she saw him, she raised herself up, and the plaits came tumbling down on her shoulders over her shirt of mail.

"Is this Sigurd, Sigmund's son, who has come carrying Fafnir's wealth in his hands?" she said.

"It is one of the Volsungs, who has done that deed," he answered. And his breath came fast as he spoke, for she was very fair. "I have heard, king's daughter, of your beauty and wisdom, of which I would make trial. But I would know first why you sleep here in the midst of fire."

"I shall sleep here no more," she said, "for Sigurd, Sigmund's son, has broken the spell which Odin put on me. Sigurd who has slain Fafnir knows not the name of fear."

She put her hand on his and drew him to the couch beside her.

"Teach me your wisdom," he said.

So she taught him the wisdom of runes. She taught him what signs must be cut on a

sword hilt to make a warrior victorious; what words must be carved on a ship to save it from harm; what marks must be set on a mead cup to keep man from woman's guile. Branch runes for healing she taught him, and thought runes for thinking, and speech runes for power over men. Runes for glass and gold and silver, runes for shield and wheel and sleigh—all this she taught him and much more besides. And when she had done, Brynhild said:

"None is wiser than you, and you answer most to my desire. I would take you first, though I had all men to choose from. But it is not fated that we should dwell together. For I am Brynhild, the shield-maiden, and I wear my helmet among princes of battle. I must give aid to them in war."

"Be that as it may," Sigurd said, "I swear by the gods that I shall have you, or no woman else!"

"And I will have none but you," she answered.

And Sigurd gave her a gold ring and mounted Grani and rode through the fire and away.

THE MAGIC DRINK

Sigurd rode on and on until he came to a town. There he sought out cunning craftsmen, and he commanded them, saying:

"Fashion me a shirt of mail of pure gold."

And they did. Then he had his shield washed all over with red gold, and a dragon painted on it, dark brown above and bright red below. And in the same manner he had his helmet marked and his saddle and coat. All his weapons he had adorned with gold, and on each was a dragon wrought.

Then he dressed himself in all his armor, and rode on with the gold that he had taken from Fafnir. And so he came to the hall of King Gjuki. The King's men saw Sigurd as he approached, and one ran and told the King and said:

"I think that a god has come here. For he is all trapped out in gold, and his horse is far greater than other horses, and most beautiful

157

are his weapons. And he himself far surpasses other men."

The King hastened out with his retainers and gave Sigurd fair greeting. Then he asked, "Who are you?"

"I am called Sigurd, son of King Sigmund," was Sigurd's answer.

"You are welcome here," King Gjuki said and took him into the hall. "Receive of us all things that you will."

And they served him well, and Sigurd abode there in high favor. For it was not possible to know Sigurd and not love him, so courteous he was and so skilled in speech. It was ever his delight to test himself in high deeds, and to take from his foes and give to his friends. Gunnar and Hogni, the King's two elder sons, rode with Sigurd and made much of him though he surpassed them in every feat. And the eyes of fair Gudrun, the King's daughter, were tender when she looked at Sigurd.

Now the Queen found out how much Sigurd loved Brynhild and marked how often he spoke of her. And she thought:

"It would be better if he were wedded to Gudrun and remained with us and we had the strength of his arm. Moreover, he has a great store of wealth, more than men ever heard of before."

So one evening, as they sat and drank, the Queen said, "Sigurd, we delight in your dwelling here, and wish you all good things. Take this horn and drink!"

He took it and drank. And because of that magic drink he could no longer remember Brynhild. The fire, his oath, and the ring he had given her all were blotted from his memory, as though he had never seen her.

SIGURD TAKES A WIFE

AFTER that Queen Grimhild went to King Gjuki and put her arms about his neck and said, "Here has come to us the greatest hero that may be found. Marry our daughter to him and let him find his delight here so that he will never depart."

"It is not the custom," the King answered, "to make offer of one's daughter. But there is more honor in offering her to him than in receiving other men's bidding. I will talk to Gunnar and Hogni about it."

So he did, and they were of one mind.

"Sigurd has done us great service and given much strength to the realm," they said. "Also he is wise in counsel and skilled in speech."

"Speak to him, then," King Gjuki said. "Offer him your sister."

Then the brothers went to Sigurd, and Gunnar said, "We will do all things, Sigurd, if you will stay here with us. We offer you both the realm and our sister, which none other might have though he begged and pleaded them of us."

And Sigurd said, "My thanks for the great honor you do me! I will take what you offer."

So a splendid feast was held, and Sigurd was wedded to Gudrun. There were games and merrymaking of every sort, and each day surpassed the one before.

Afterwards Gunnar and Hogni swore blood-brotherhood with Sigurd, as though they had been born of one mother. And they journeyed over the land together and brought home great stores of booty. And ever it was Sigurd's delight to give aid to Gunnar and Hogni.

THE WOOING OF BRYNHILD

Now Queen Grimhild had learned by her magic arts that Brynhild excelled all women. She went to Gunnar and said to him:

"All things are well with you, my son, but one. You are without a wife. Woo Brynhild! That is the best match for you."

Gunnar answered, "She is said to be fair indeed, and I am not unwilling."

He spoke to his father and brothers and to Sigurd, and they all urged it upon him.

"I will ride with you," Sigurd said, "and help you all I can."

"And I, too," said Hogni.

So they made skillful preparation, and Sigurd and Hogni went with Gunnar. They rode over dale and hill. At last they came to the hall of King Budli, Brynhild's father, and to him they made the offer of marriage.

"I am willing," King Budli said, "if Brynhild will consent. But she has taken an oath that she will wed only the man who will ride through the flaming fire that surrounds her hall."

"Fire will not stop me," Gunnar said. "With your consent I will go and woo her."

So they rode on, and after a time they found Brynhild's hall, all roofed with gold and with fiery flames burning about it.

"Wait here," Gunnar said to his brother and Sigurd.

And he spurred his horse, Goti, on towards the fire. But when Goti felt the heat of the flames, he drew back. Spur as he would, Gunnar could not make the horse go into the fire.

"Why do you retreat?" Sigurd called out to Gunnar.

"My steed will not go into the fire!" Gunnar said. "Lend me your Grani, for there is no horse like him. He knows not fear."

"You are free to take him," Sigurd said.

So Gunnar mounted Grani and pricked him with his spurs and urged him on with voice and hand. But Grani would not stir.

"He will go only for you," Gunnar said at last.

"Then let us change shapes as your mother Grimhild has taught us," Sigurd said. "And I will ride through the fire and woo Brynhild for you."

So they changed shapes. Afterwards Sigurd rode forward, and except that the sword Gram was in his hand, none might tell he was not Gunnar. But Grani knew. When Sigurd pricked him with his golden spurs, Grani leaped forward into the fire. There was a great noise and the flames were stirred violently, the earth shook, and the fire rose up to the very heavens. Then it died down. And on the other side Sigurd faced the hall and the closed door.

He threw open the door. Within sat Brynhild on her high-seat, like a swan on the wave, all clad in armor and with a sword by her side. But Sigurd knew her not, so powerful was the drink he had drunk.

"Who are you?" she asked.

"I am Gunnar, Gjuki's son," Sigurd answered. "And you are granted me to be my wife, with your father's consent, if I should ride through your flickering flames according to your choosing."

Then Brynhild's heart sank within her. For she had thought only Sigurd would dare come to her through the fire.

"I scarcely know what I should answer," she said.

And Sigurd said, "In return for this I shall pay a great dowry in gold and fine treasure."

"Gunnar!" she cried. "Do not speak to me of such things unless you are the foremost of all men. For I do not wish to wed. I have gone into battle and such things are still my desire."

Sigurd said, "Great deeds have you done. But now you must call to mind your oath, that if any man should ride through this fire, you would follow him."

She said it was true. She made him welcome, and he wooed her. He took from her finger the ring he had given her before, and in its place he gave her another ring from Fafnir's treasure.

After that Sigurd rode away through the same fire. He and Gunnar changed shapes again, and they returned home. A feast was now made ready. King Budli came with Brynhild his daughter, and the rejoicings lasted many days.

And when the marriage feast was over, Sigurd remembered his oaths to Brynhild. He remembered the cliff, the ring of fire, the rampart of shields, and the wisdom she had taught him. But he made no sign.

"AWAKE, BRYNHILD!"

BRYNHILD believed she had kept her oath. She believed she had married the man who had ridden through the fire to her. But she had no joy of Gunnar, for she had given her heart to Sigurd long before.

Now one day she was with Gudrun, Sigurd's wife. And she saw on Gudrun's finger the ring which she herself had so long worn and which Sigurd had afterwards taken from her. She turned pale as though she were dead. For she knew then that she had been deceived and that it was Sigurd who had come to her through the flames in Gunnar's shape.

After that Brynhild took to her bed. She would neither eat nor drink.

"What ails you, dear wife?" Gunnar asked her with concern.

Brynhild had never been too happy with

Gunnar, but now she hated him, and she answered him with great bitterness.

"I swore an oath when I was at home with my father," she said, "that I would wed the man who would ride through the fire to me. For I thought that Sigurd alone could do it. But you deceived me. Now I care not to live, for Sigurd is not mine and I have broken my oath. Nevermore shall you see me glad in your hall. You shall never see me drink, or play chess, or speak what is in my thoughts, or embroider fair stuffs with gold, or give you counsel."

She would not leave her bed, nor speak to anyone.

And so six days passed.

"Sigurd," Gunnar said at last, for he despaired of Brynhild's life, "you go to her. Perhaps she will speak to you."

But Sigurd made no answer. He knew well enough what ailed Brynhild.

The next day when he came home from the hunt, Sigurd said to his wife, "It seems to me that Brynhild's fever is very heavy, and she will die of it."

"My lord," Gudrun answered, "she has now slept seven days and no one has dared to awaken her."

"She is not asleep," Sigurd said, "but is planning fearful things against me."

"Go to her, then," Gudrun said, "and speak to her and see if her anger may not be lessened. Give her gold and soften her wrath."

Sigurd went out. Brynhild's door was open, and he entered and stood by her bed, where she lay with closed eyes. He thought she was asleep, and he said:

"Awake, Brynhild! the sun is shining over all the town, and you have slept long enough. Cast off your sorrow and be glad."

She opened her eyes, and there came rushing in upon her the memory of that other time when he had come to her and said, "Awake!" And she scorned his gay words, for her heart was filled with bitterness for things that could never be.

"How is it that you dare to come and see me?" she said. "None deceived me worse than you."

Sigurd knew that it was true. He wanted to defend himself, but all his skill in speech

had left him. He could only say, "Why will you not speak to those about you? What troubles you?"

At that she poured out her woe. "I will tell you the cause of my wrath," she said. "Gunnar did not ride through the fire to me. I wondered then at the man who came into my hall, and I thought I recognized your eyes. But the truth was hidden from me, and now it is too late!"

"I am no nobler than Gunnar," Sigurd said. "It is a strange thing to have no love for such a king. But what is it that troubles you most?"

"Most bitter of all my woes is that I can not stain a sword with your blood!" Brynhild answered.

"Have no fear," Sigurd said. "In a short time from now a sword will indeed stand in my heart, and you yourself will not live long after me."

"I care not a bit for my life!" Brynhild said bitterly.

"Do not say that!" Sigurd said. "I would give all my wealth if only you would not die!"

"Too late you come to tell me that my suffering distresses you," she said. "Now I have no comfort of it."

"Brynhild!" Sigurd cried. And so greatly were his sides swollen with grief that the rings of his mailed shirt burst. "Rather than that you should die, I will take you and leave Gudrun."

"I desire you not," she said, "you so full of deceit—nor any other."

"SLAY SIGURD!"

AND NOW Brynhild had no other wish than to destroy Sigurd. Night and day she thought of it, and at last she opened her lips to Gunnar.

"Slay Sigurd!" she said. "If you do not, I shall go home to my kinsmen."

When Gunnar heard that, it seemed to him that the earth rocked under his feet. He was pulled this way and that and knew not what to think or say or do.

"I love Sigurd," he thought. "I am bound to him by the oath of brotherhood I swore. But I cannot let Brynhild go. I could not endure the grief, nor the shame."

In his trouble he sought out Hogni his brother.

Hogni said, "Neither you nor I can do the deed, for we have sworn a blood bond with Sigurd. But our brother Gutthorm has not. Let us urge him to slay Sigurd and we will promise him great honor in return."

So they plotted with Gutthorm. And towards morning, when Sigurd lay in his bed asleep, Gutthorm went in and thrust his sword into the Volsung so deep that the point of it stood in the bolster under him.

Sigurd awoke when he felt the wound. Gram lay by the side of his bed. He seized the sword and cast it after Gutthorm. And it struck Gutthorm in the back and cut him asunder, so that half his body fell one way and half another.

Then Sigurd raised himself up on the pillow to speak to Gudrun, who, all covered with his blood, wept and lamented.

"Weep not, Gudrun," Sigurd said. "Your brothers still live to comfort you. It is Brynhild who has done this, she who loved me more than any other man."

With that, Sigurd died. And Brynhild laughed aloud when she saw Gudrun weep.

TOGETHER IN DEATH

Afterwards all men looked at Brynhild in wonder. For none could understand why she now lamented with laughter the deed she had ordered with tears.

She bade a great store of gold to be brought, and summoned to her all who wished to receive riches of her. And when they were come, she took a sword and stabbed herself. And she fell against her pillows and said, "Let each who will take from this gold."

Then she turned to Gunnar, her husband. "I make you one last prayer," she said.

"Have a funeral pyre made on the level plain for all of us—for Sigurd and me and for those that will be slain with him. Burn me there. Our burial shall not be poor if there attend us also the five maids and eight slaves that my father gave me. I will say no more, for my wound is open and gushing."

So a great pyre was built, and the body of Sigurd was laid upon it. And when the pyre was all ablaze, Brynhild went out upon it and was burnt there with Sigurd.

So was their oath kept in death that was broken in life.

INDEX

du faint
giziae .
moust n
merueu
que au
in nou
rent qu

MAD
MBDB
OfA2O

HOUY
2IMOE
HOFAI2
OBVAO

2OIAM
2ENN
A†MP
1958

hpod gap ma
betm scyldinga ic
Inne cide cmbe
pe5ende pear hu
caldro dep . ecz pa
hazen. dcin to hofi